In Bob Arnold's *Sunswumthru A Building* a poet shares his memories and well-hewn meditations on the various tools he has used in handcrafting the life and maintaining the homestead he shares with his wife Susan. In a day when almost all poets are to be found in the halls of academe, this is a book of wilderness building with its close-to-the earth perspective and a deep appreciation of those from whom he learned his own skills.

As companion volume to the author's popular earlier book *On Stone, a builder's notebook*, it takes the reader as passenger in a work truck from the smallest jobs, to building sites, to the evolution of friendships. Within the poet's story of the building of a cottage with his home schooled son Carson, Bob Arnold reflects on many learning experiences for both father and son.

Bob Arnold's background derives from five generations of a lumber business family settled in the Berkshire Hills of Massachusetts and now dwelling in Vermont. With on-site illustrations by Scotland's Laurie Clark, the poet's prose cuts a trail into familial woodlands. Come in for a visit.

Sunswumthru A Building

to Bob + Dot -
TOOLS iN HAND -
ASCVEK.
Rocko AKNOTS

BOB ARNOLD

Sunswumthru A Building

WITH DRAWINGS BY LAURIE CLARK

ORIGIN PRESS

A CHARLES SANDY BOOK

Origin Press has published books since the early 1950s
from Boston and Kyoto by & for & in
the memory of Cid Corman.

ORIGIN PRESS books are distributed by
Longhouse, Publishers & Booksellers
1604 River Road, Guilford, Vermont 05301
poetry@sover.net
http://www.LonghousePoetry.com

Library of Congress Cataloging-in-Publication Data

Arnold, Bob
  Sunswumthru a building / Bob Arnold ; with drawings by Laurie Clark.
    p. cm.
  ISBN 1-929048-06-8 (alk. paper)
  1. House construction Vermont Anecdotes. 2.
Carpentry Tools Anecdotes. 3. Arnold, Bob, 1952 Homes and
haunts Anecdotes. 4. Poets Vermont Homes and haunts Anecdotes.
I. Title.
  TH4812.A735 2006
  690'.837092--dc22

                                2006021406

for those along the way picked-up
in a half-century work crew—
Carson, Becky, & Susan Arnold—
my brother Scott, Ron Taylor,
workmate David Emmons, &
in the memory of Jim Duffy,
David Scott, & Hap Weatherhead

Every spirit builds itself a house;
and beyond its house a world;
and beyond its world, a heaven.
Know then, that the world exists for you.

— EMERSON

CONTENTS

IMPOSSIBLE WITHOUT

Susan Arnold who read and lived with every speck of jobs, rough in the field, and later all writing and revisions. That's a valentine. Chuck Sandy who came and said he wanted to publish this book, and then proved it. Invaluable. Jonathan Greene and Dobree Adams for all fine points, suggestions, design ruminations for the book. Pure wisdom. Hayden Carruth for cracking the whip, and Kirpal Gordon for telling the truth. Real stuff. Thomas A. Clark for reading this book like a long walk into his Scottish wilds, carefully. And Laurie Clark for equally the same, plus for asking, "May I do the illustrations?" All a gift from this family. Peggy Carey for decades of family friendship and letting me build her house. And Ethan Heicher who published an earlier version of the chapter *Sunswumthru A Building* as a limited edition book he made with his two hands. My kin. For Carson Arnold, who as a young boy, once upon a time, stole my heart.

Sunswumthru A Building

BUILDING BOOKS

Of all toolboxes yanked from trucks, or automobile trunks, lifted out of back seats, or even carried in as a canvas bag, I never saw a book tucked away in one. A book is about the last thing ever spotted on a job site, and usually it is a tossed away manual for some equipment. But I read books on the job — sandwich in one hand, Bashō in the other hand. I would carry my books in my lunch pail. Because I was always reading, I often earned the nickname "Preacher."

So it isn't any accident I still bring books to my building job sites, now thirty-five years at it and going strong. I started out as a boy carpenter working for my family lumber business and those jobs were mostly modern quick-built homes. A dynamo crew could nail up a half-dozen homes over one summer. I soon moved to Vermont and worked with building crews here or there, but really I worked best alone or with one companion helper. There were countless old homes I worked on, repairing stonework to carpentry. One of my strangest jobs was helping an owner build his large house — mostly I was there to show him how to frame and he would carry on when I had to be away — though his one demand for the house was that he wanted no windows, just a front door. Since he lived the greater part of the year at a university job far from his new home, he was wary of vandals and wanted to keep any out by keeping any windows out. That was until I reminded him how

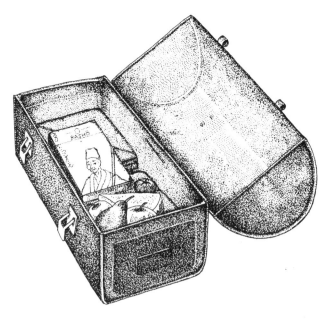

vandals could just as easily chain saw an entry into his house to rummage inside, steel door or not. On hearing that, he agreed to put a few windows in. Small ones. Since this friend was a university librarian, we talked books and writers from sun up to sun down on the job and then on the long drives he gave me back to my home.

In the year 2000, I began to build a cottage on our land with my fifteen-year-old son, Carson. A two-story, timber-framed, steel-roofed and wooden side-shingled building, boxed out with many windows since I have been storing salvaged windows from other jobs for years. No better place to draw the daylight and save on wall material. The cottage hunched on a wide stone ledge and was a complete bugger to hand lay dry stone upon and under the building frame, but we did. A month long chore. And during that time Carson and I talked music and books and films and even reminisced about the trips we did together as a family on trains, and we also fought and fussed a little because it was hot work and because we are father and son. Building this cottage together—twelve feet wide by eighteen feet long—would be the first leg of Carson's home school studies. A program that kept him happily away from the local high school and into percolating sessions of book learning and back work earning, as they once used to say. When Carson asks which books meant the most to me as a builder—including the books I would bring along to jobs as companions—whether they had anything to do with building or not, these are the ones that always spring to mind. A neat dozen. Someday, we will have these books on a shelf in the cottage when we're done.

1. *Working and Thinking on the Waterfront* by Eric Hoffer (real worker/real writer)

2. *The Long-Legged House* by Wendell Berry (real farmer/ real writer)

3. *Payne Hollow* by Harlan Hubbard (husband & wife homesteading quiet team)

4. *The Rock Is My Home* by Werner Blaser (my bible for stone work and its environment)

5. *Indians in Overalls* by Jaime de Angulo (no better writer to start you at dirt level)

6. *The Granite Pail* by Lorine Niedecker (no better poet for the fine point flowing details)

7. *The Selected Letters of Robinson Jeffers* ed. by Ann N. Ridgeway (who made his West Coast days around legends & stone)

8. *The Celtic Twilight* by W. B. Yeats (this could be interchanged with Synge's *The Aran Islands*: both ultimate, tidy, lunch pail companions)

9. *The Sign of Jonas* by Thomas Merton (the other ultimate, tidy, lunch pail companion)

10. *Ian Hamilton Finlay* by Yves Abreioux (in the evening, after work, to sit and visit with this craftsman's world)

11. *A Pattern Language* by Christopher Alexander et al (no better on towns, buildings, construction worldwide)

12. *The Folk Songs of North America* by Alan Lomax (because there should be a song in your working head)

CODA

Now getting older with my bad back blues, I have made a new friend in a Chinese gentleman named Dr. Xu. He speaks difficult English but we talk in body gestures and words. And since he knows I'm a builder he has asked me questions about how to fix things. Being fearless, he is a great learner. He shared with me the other day how he put a section of new roofing on his house. He would climb up in short sessions —tucking some shingles under his arm—and bang nails on his one day off each week. He was a little leery of the ladder but his devoted wife held that for him. It wasn't hard at all, he assured me. The first thing he did was to go to his local library to find a book on roofing and its procedures, and then he began.

A FAVORITE OUTDOOR TOOL

While working for a living with tools, there must be easily a hundred to recall for comment. Sure there are. My son Carson, who often works with me, was certain I would choose the peavey. He has seen us work that grand pivot-stick to wise purchase—tossing a tree log over, often one heavier than the woodstove inside our house—impossible tasks accomplished. But it's not the peavey this time. Nor my dear wood-splitting maul I visit almost every morning, bound-taped thick around the handle under the heavy head. Or my hammers—mostso the hatchet hammer for cedar shingles, a virtuoso of hammers. Not the many rakes, shovels, iron bars for my stone work, or even my wheelbarrows that move the field stone from one place to another. They also moved so many yards of crushed stone, firewood by the decades, groceries from a far off parked truck in the pith of deep woods winter snows. And my son, when much younger, hopped in for many rides in this wheelbarrow. So did his mother. But the tool that rode the most with me, the one I learned from as a novice woodcutter coming off a pair of long Swedish bow saws, and I just had to make my way into teaching myself the ropes and earn my living cutting trees, was my Jonsered-90 chain saw. Big bold red hefty *mother*, but it cut like no other saw I ever handled. Twenty-inch cutting bar. I've had too many close calls with limbs, kickback stumps, pinched base cuts and never anyone around to talk, bitch, moan with about it all, except the Jonsered-90. And talk we did; as I also talked to each tree I cut, especially the handsome and full headdress beauties. Many winters I could be found hiking away from the house with a backpack of fuel jugs, wedges, an ax, and the Jonsered slung over my shoulder carried up a hill that way. Bought in 1977 from a guy who ran a small engine business in his barn, and I'm sure he looked at me and then the saw and thought for sure trouble was ahead. True, I tore two knuckles to the bone when my hand slipped across the sharp chain when unlocking nuts for the bar. I was surprised the Jonsered would do this to me, or did I do it to myself? Between the saw and myself, we talked this way. There were no other accidents, though hundreds of jobs ahead that paid for the saw many times over. Until, one day dropping roadside trees—making a better clearing for a forest yard—the Jonsered snarled and cut and worked well, and then wouldn't start. Busted piston. It made it to almost twenty-five years. Oh sure, I babied the saw to keep it all those years. I have logger friends that go through chain saws like work boots. But like I said, this was a friend. The saw now sits on an upper shelf in my tool room because it's heavy and I'm older, and I've been told there are much lighter and faster saws now on the market. But do they talk and listen?

A FAVORITE INDOOR TOOL

What indoor tool haven't I been able to make an outdoor tool? I can't think of any. There are five portable typewriters I've collected over the years and with these I wrote five prose books. A plucky, old Smith Corona that I used to write my book *On Stone*; each day coming in from outdoor work and trying to save an hour or two to write another chapter. But I also wrote with one of my portable typewriters outdoors— took one with me in 1975 to Newfoundland in an equally old VW bug and would type postcards to friends on the roof of the car, or on the deck of the ferry sailing over. However, no matter how much I love my old typewriters, they aren't my choice for a favorite indoor tool. That goes to my portable (and "portable" is the key word for all indoor tools) record player. Housed in its soft leather brown case, it plays 45s and 33s but I only play the latter and own thousands. The record player's $14 stylus is easily replaceable from the Crosley Company. It was my friend Marie Harris who raved about its merits and I believed her, and before I knew it, Susan surprised me with one for my birthday. Since then it has played music in every room of the house. The unit has a long attached cord to plug in, so I can have it playing as far away from the house as 300 feet off three extension cord lengths. I have taken it to carpentry jobs with a circular saw, table saw and the record player juiced off the same power cord... Nina Simone, John

Fahey, Skip James high enough away from the dust and commotion but spinning and serenading nonetheless. When done for the day, wrap the tools up, and move everything undercover. Stack the sawhorses. Rake up scraps. Close the lid on the record player and snap it shut.

CHAIN SAWS

It was Eck Finlay of Scotland who asked me to write two short essays on tools—an outdoor favorite and an indoor— that set me sailing on this idea of a small book on tools. A modest primer about the tools I used during all sorts of jobs in my livelihood from stone work, carpentry, house building, landscape jobs, tree work, farm work, plus the writing and bookseller trades. After I finished the essay on my Jonsered-90, I figured it was only fair to report further on what chain saw I am using now. Back then when the piston busted on the 90, I had already been saving for a newer and lighter saw—or at least the commonsense side of me was saving— because I would need as large and as fast a saw as the 90. But I still had my smaller limbing saw, Jonsered-49. I just didn't use it much. For some reason, maybe because the 49 knew the 90 was always around and dependable as the sun rising, it would act stubborn and fussy with me whenever I came to use it. So it collected dust in the tool room, and I would even use the beefier 90 to limb, cut saplings, do all the small tree work the 49 was bought for. For awhile there, I did use both saws. I even took the saws to Bob Ormond's chain saw shop in Shelburne, Massachusetts to have him install chain-brakes since neither saw came with one back in the good old days of less regulations and riding by the seat of your pants. Ormond was a good worker, a big machine operator, who did chain saw

29

repairs on the side, in a garage off from his house. He had his son working with him and they would take up one half of the garage, heads always bent over their long worktable gunked with saw parts, special tools, and two distinct personalities. Bob was all business. You paid him top dollar for his work so he wasn't there to waste your time. On the other hand, his son was still living at home—a friendly smile and goofy with stories about his real passion, turkey hunting. He had hunting trophies spangled all around his work area, so an hour or two could drift by waiting for him to do saw repairs and all the while plugging his mouth with chewing tobacco, practicing his turkey calls, sharing photographs of bird kills and amounting a pretty good service bill for you. But he sold me on the Jonsered-49, and probably the two Ormonds saved my neck, insisting on the chain-brakes, and twenty years later I'm still using the 49. It starts like a charm without the 90 anywhere in sight. Just this past winter my son and I cleared deadwood and stragglers on the steep riverbank right across from our house. Even though we ended up half the time in the river wearing high rubber boots tending to wild falls of a few trees, and wanting everything to look right with brush piled along the riverbank, where ice would form quickly. We were just after a better view of the river, without losing the distinction of some lofty hemlocks and oak trees. Maybe I'm thinking twice about replacing this saw quite so soon. Today, at a flat three-below-zero at noontime, we went out into the woodlot to scout up a few standing dead elm trees—the few that are still around. I have cut almost every elm over thirty years on the property but somehow have missed one or two. And sure enough, we found a pair—bark almost all fallen off and dry as a bone, ready to burn. I went back to the house and warmed up both myself and the Jonsered-49 by the woodstove because both of us like that sort of thing now. My son doesn't mind it either. In a few minutes we would hike out to the woodlot, cut down both elm trees, buck them stove length and carry it all back indoors with a canvas satchel. It would be perfect wood for the kitchen cookstove for the next week. Just me, my son, and the Jonsered-49.

OTHER TREE SAWS

I have to tell you there were other saws I used before the Jonsered duo, but I almost forget them. I started off learning on a 16-inch bar Homelite—the light blue color model. I was given the saw by a minister I befriended in the early 70s when I ended up living in a rural cabin he owned by a larger red colonial farmhouse that he also owned. I was there as his caretaker. The Homelite chain saw came with the job. The problem was I was twenty years old and just beginning to learn how to fell trees with bow saws. I was the proud owner of two bow saws but never quite learned how to sharpen the blades, and would simply replace one as it dulled. I would toss the dull blades over my tall woodpile in the back of the woodshed since that wood was never used. Part of my Yankee sensibility of never-ever burning wood that you should cut today. As wood was burned, more was always cut, and I would forever be two years ahead. The bow saws always churning. In my twenties no snow was deep enough, no cold cold enough, no tree big enough. I came to work on tree jobs with the two bow saws as if it was the biggest joke in all the world, and I'd be there two days pulling away on the bow saws, when a chain saw would have the same job polished off in a few hours. It's funny how we all learn. But I always imagined the patience and stubborn belief that working with the bow saws was the precursor of how I could also hike twelve miles from my cabin in the woods to town; cut house sill timbers with handsaws; open 100 foot long driveways with a snow shovel; lug flat stone after stone up the bank from the river by hand and set into countless wheelbarrow loads, and push these loads home to build a forty foot rock terrace. Never mind waiting for workmanlike lines of poetry to gel. The bow saws were my best teachers for moving me on to the chain saws. The Homelite. A McCullough I owned for awhile that appeared suddenly, and as suddenly was gone — probably a loaner. A small Poulan that came, in its case, as payment for cleaning out someone's barn. On the same job I also carried away a Toulouse-Lautrec print, nicely framed. The Poulan never did much for me — too small, lousy color, it seemed more like a toy. So I used the Homelite until I drove it to the brink of extinction. Dropped a tree, or something, on its handle and had to have a spare part, and a different color, fitted on. It always looked like a mongrel after that. I knew a bit of my bow saw discipline was lost when years after working with chain saws, I was up in the woods with the Homelite, depth of winter, and it decided no to start. Forget it. Dead as doornails. I got so fit to be tied that I dropped the saw onto the ground and ended up kicking it with the side of my boot all the way back to the house. Talking to it, of course. And when I got there, I left the poor saw out in the snow for awhile and grabbed both bow saws and tramped back to the woods to finish the job. Much slower. Much harder. Much quieter.

WEDGES

I have never used a wood-splitter. It seems a whole other frame of mind. And I have never met a block of wood— elm, locust, oak, no matter—that I haven't been able to split with a wedge. Maybe two wedges. And for the real ball-busters, three wedges. Make sure you buy a good size woodstove with a chunk-size door on it and you can ride by with almost anything. I remember how pros, who really know how to use wedges, could drop a tree on a dime. I can use a wedge and fell a tree in the right direction. I have been hired to drop trees even linemen walked away from. Real thrillers—like a huge oak somehow still standing and leaning heavy on a river bank and it has to be dropped for a new utility line blazing through. No need for wedges there but the tension on the tree is spectacular to live through, gunning into making the back cut. You think right then and there—maybe, you and the tree, both—are going to die. I had a mammoth sugar maple once split in half on me midway through the stump cut, and all I could do was stand still and hope I was thin enough to squeak into whatever passage was left for me. It's humbling when the tree takes over. In another book, I described watching a co-worker drop my Homelite chain saw from high in an elm tree we were limbing and then felling, and all I could do was watch the saw flip over many times in the air—so majestically for a heavy tool—and land like a sword, bar first into the ground. Saved! On that job, when it came time to drop the tree, we suddenly ran out of wedges. Three disappeared quickly into the meaty wood. So I ran down the road and around a corner to a house where I had worked as caretaker tending horses, and I knew the barn and the right door and my way around to the tools, and found one more wedge—plastic and yellow and rather simple looking—and when I ran it back, it took the tree down.

PEAVEY

Now it's the peavey's turn. A primitive common sense tool if there ever was one. Thick bull handle about as tall as my son when he was thirteen years old and he would run to fetch it for me. Harpoon shaped point to position into the side of a tree log, with its swinging hook to grab hold of what's to move. It isn't complicated, but you do want to let it do what it wants to do as momentum starts. If you use two, it must be something, though I only own one. When I need another, the closest tool I have are the iron bars I use for stonework, and they're pretty persuasive. I also like the sound of the word peavey. It seems made for a much smaller tool, and at the same time, mysteriously anachronistic. Most of the people in the world still have no idea what the word means and what the tool is. It stands up by the woodshed door as if an important ax in a fire alarm box—there for you, if needed—and when really needed, you'll know it, and go fetching. It has only one purpose—moving something that is stronger than you. I bought my peavey from a mail order logging outfit from northern California—land of tall redwoods and exotic big-man catalogs—it came along with an extremely handy duo gas/oil fuel jug for chain saws, hard-hat with face screen (since busted off) and earmuffs, plus a zippered work jersey that still fits. The peavey arrived, as is, with a large mailing label stuck fast to its handle. It looked pretty cool coming out of the UPS truck that way. Since I never got the hang of handling a come-along, the peavey is the best I know—short of using my truck with a rope or chain—at moving that certain heavy something in the way.

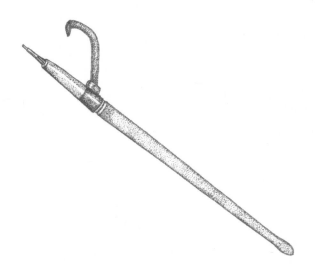

SPLITTING-MAUL

To my mind, it is unthinkable to think of living in the north woods without a splitting-maul—even if you don't use a woodstove. Maul is one of those words that goes along with the back country—like shovel, boots, ax—and the splitting-maul is more diverse than the ax. I own both, plus three other sledgehammers all of different head weights and usage. The splitting-maul is a many-faceted tool, able to be used on either end as the handler gets proficient with the tool. It splits wood better than any ax. It's a driven wedge coming down through the air for goodness sakes, and once you get cracking with it, the flip side is a sledgehammer head that can whack in splitting wedges all day long if you wish. Figure to go through one handle with your new splitting-maul if you've never used one before. You'll bust up the first handle in good shape developing your aim with the firewood. After you replace the handle with your final handle for life—meaning, you have a steady aim now with your splitting—you will begin to wonder how you made it along in life this long without the tool. SUVs, cell phones, credit cards all look like silly business if you're really living in the woods. And if you bust up this second handle, you are: loaning the tool out too much, have a rotten aim, or are not cut out to split wood. My first and last maul was given to me by the same minister who supplied my caretaking tools of a used chain saw, old extension ladder, and a few other items. This was well over thirty years ago. Within a year I had destroyed the handle teaching myself the fine art of wood splitting. I then burned the old handle out of the wedge eye, bought a new and longer handle and began to teach others how to split wood. I was also hired to split wood for an elderly couple, a job that would last twenty years. It was six cords of firewood for their needs each winter and almost every stick had to be trimmed down either for their handling ease, or how they insisted on using a drafty old cookstove as a novelty item. I didn't argue—they were paying me. And I do know they liked their tea warmed up on the cookstove while having breakfast or lunch by its side— with their modern kitchen, oil furnace, and an Audi in the carport under the old barn. When the couple sold their farm and my job of twenty years was finished, I was offered to take any tools from the barn I wished. I liked some of the wooden maple sugar pails, the handmade apple picker's ladder, the two-man saw, and of course my splitting-maul. With its dandy fiberglass handle. Its splitting head worn smooth and sure.

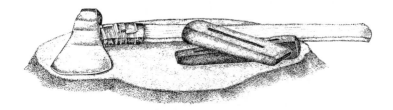

AWL & CORDLESS DRILL

The awl is a funny tool, it's always spilling out of my leather nail apron. It doesn't quite fit down into one of the narrow pockets on the apron with nail-sets and a thick pencil stub in the way. And when it gets thrown in with the nails—out of my loss where to go with it—after awhile it's in the way of my hand reaching in grabbing nails and out it drops down the ladder or sliding a long length of steel roof. That's where I have used the awl the most—punching pilot holes for the screws that fasten down steel roofing. Work goes zip /zip if you have a worker using the awl and lining up the screw pattern with another worker following with the cordless drill. I came late to the cordless drill—typically, hanging in longer than most with my electric drills owned for ages and all the unwinding of cords and sticking with the old ways. Foolishly. The cordless drill has almost become what the hammer is—an independent servant who can go anywhere with you, provided you keep an eye on changing the battery and don't drop it from the roof. It will make you think twice about using your screwdrivers, and I own a toolbox of those and still like using each one. It takes me back to that quiet, slower process. But most of the time I am reaching for the cordless drill to remove hinges, shank down floor planks, sand smooth the fiberglass filler for body work on a truck, and most recently to drill down four separate new steel roofs on buildings we built on the property: a full two-story cottage, then a privy, a one and half-story studio, and finally a large addition onto our house. The cordless has been busy. It's a Bosch model, and the only tool I have ever bought from Home Depot. You walk in one day out of curiosity and there's a tool sale not to be matched on this cordless drill and you walk out with it. End of story. Go to work. It comes with a hard case. Many steel roofs later, and like most of my tools, it has become an old friend. The drill hasn't let me down. I haven't dropped it. It works and works and works all day in the hot sun with me setting screws right. Only the tiny switch for changing the rotary direction has snapped off, but par for the course after four years of duty. I can shift its directions with a screwdriver, or with my awl, if I want to really take the time to get its sharp point on what's left of the shifting switch. As for the awl, when not with me, it's with Susan, who has begun using it as the perfect tool to make the starter holes in books we print and sew by hand.

FOUR-FOOT LEVEL

I own two of these, plus its companion two-foot level, and then a few smaller old models that have minimal use, with busted glass sockets or bubbles—but I can't throw them out. Plus there's the plumber's small torpedo level that is used more than one would think. So the four-foot levels are always with me on stonework jobs just for that certain leveling that I want certain, and where the eye, for a change, isn't quite trusted. Or I want a second opinion. Both levels are wood models, framed with a metal edge. One came as a birthday gift from Susan years ago, and the other was bought for a song from a friend at one of his many tag sales when he was once more moving from the area "for good." I picked up windows from him when he left for Phoenix, a wheelbarrow when he left for New Hampshire, this level and other fine tools when he finally picked up and headed for Florida and has stayed put there. I think he priced everything low for me since we worked together building a few houses, and he wanted—like I did—to see the tools with me, so we were sort of working together (tool-wise), as always. I bought the level to have my friend with me but I really didn't need another one. Though in a way I did. I now catch myself deciding which level to use depending on the job—stonework, take Susan's with me. Carpentry, have David's along. He's a carpenter, so maybe something good will rub off. Unlike other builders who store their long level in a work truck behind the seat or up on the gun rack, mine hang together off a 16-common nail hook in my tool room. The other day I used one just to double-check that our washing machine was set true. Years before that, I placed the level on top of a poured dam wall I built on one of the nearby woods rivers. It's the tool that tells you at the end of the work day that everything is plumb and on the level when set against a hung door, a partition wall setup, or on a finish floor. The great settler. Just watch the bubble.

MASONRY TOOLS

Not being a mason, rather a dry wall stone builder, I rarely think about masonry tools. I own what I need and have for decades. One metal bucket of trowels of all sizes and shapes but I usually only use the same one that fits just right in my hand—no matter how large the job. I have laid up block and brick chimneys and always use this same trowel. Likewise with the joint trowel, the tool that cleans up the look of a job. I own one star-drill that I have used on occasion. A few cold chisels. Two casks of masonry nails that more often are used for pounding into stubborn wood, rather than concrete. I like my stone chisel hammer and three pound mallet and the soft brush for wiping damp mortar to achieve the right look with stone. It's a roughened texture that you want, not smooth. If I can skip using mortar with stone, I'll gladly do it. I always have a few bags of mortar mix on hand but more times than not the last bag will harden on me—just from the weather—before I remember to use it. I'm not fond of masonry, but I have laid up a few foundation walls, repaired others, pointed even more. Once I get moving with brick, it has an enjoyable flow, though only for a day or two, whereas, with dry stone I can go week after week. No masonry gimmicks around. Once upon a time there were masons who could work brick, cement and dry stone like a three-ring juggling act and do each job impeccably. Today, everything is specialized and a little ordinary. I'm not much for masonry, but I can do it. I laid a field stone hallway for someone once upon a time, and built a few brick, tile and stone hearths, and even had the embarrassing moment of being hired as a mason to tear a brick chimney down—very easy —each brick just tossed out a bedroom window, a few at a time, until I was on the first floor. And then finding out there would be another mason hired to build a replacement chimney the next day. Ah, I was young then. Ah, so what. These days I can be found taking a long morning walk in some faraway town—say in New Mexico—and catching a crew setting-up on a side street they've closed down with scaffolding, drop cloths and a mixer; and I'll stand there almost an hour, before thinking of moving, just watching the adobe masons freely work.

PRIVY

Most wouldn't consider the privy a tool, but I can't think of a better one. I remember when I was ten years old and went on job sites with my lumberman father. A bruiser of a bull-dozer operator strode over to us to say hello and showed with a sweep of his hand across the yard what he had just prepped, and then he asked my father, "By the way, Bob, where's the shitter?" Shitter, crapper, outhouse and privy, all the same difference, and out in the wilds, it's still an essential tool on the job. It also takes tools to build one, and that's exactly what my son and I did on the second structure we would build together. This time it would be a piece of cake compared to the taxing cottage job with all the similar principles of setting a building up, no matter how small. We would build this privy on the same design scheme as I used in our original cabin where Susan and I lived from 1972 to 1978; no plumbing or water line, not much electricity and all wood heat. Perfect setup for a privy. With no worry in the world of freezing any pipes except your own. The cabin privy was a side closet right out the back door. You walked in and found a plywood bench with a bucket we kept out there under the toilet seat. When done, you carried the bucket out into the weather, found the plank covering the hand-shoveled pit, lifted that, dumped your business in and brought the bucket back to the privy. Absolutely logical and no headaches. We would build this new privy much on the same design but with a smidge more ingenuity—instead of having to deal with the bucket from the inside, we dealt with the waste bucket outside from a neat little trap door that opened at the back of the building, and nearby to the dug pit, making fewer steps. We also covered the small roof with steel to best catch the rainwater runoff, and with a barrel underneath the drip-line, all the water was there to use in the bucket. If that was frozen or for some reason dry, the pond was ten feet away. The steel roof was odds and ends saved from other jobs and not all the same color. So one hot day Carson and I climbed up there and took turns brushing on two coats of forest green enamel paint to best match the green cottage roof. We matched it pretty close. The building was four foot square, and set up on 4x4 sills left over from the cottage rafters, sided with white cedar shingles and built on hefty corner stones. Studded up with three windows to catch the finest natural light, plus a Dutch door to add more daylight if needed, or privacy, but always that unique touch Dutch doors offer. The windows are all fixed barn sashes. One had a crack in the glass, so I stenciled a line of ivy plants running as the crack went along, and it almost disappeared. There is no insulation, since the structure is small and of temporary use; instead we tack up favorite pictures and snapshot postcards and general visuals a sitting visitor to the place might enjoy. The privy is placed and built exactly in between the cottage and the house, so wherever one is in a lurch, the privy is there.

LADDER

No matter who you are, almost everyone has used a ladder
and will use one again. Getting upstairs is really a ladder, of
sorts. In my first cabin, that's how I climbed to the upstairs
—until Susan moved in—and a woman you fall in love with
will always inspire improvement, if but for her own use. So
I built a real stairway instead of the ladder but we still had
to climb it like a ladder since it was so steep. I've owned my
favorite ladder for over thirty years, and it isn't anything to
look at—just a sixteen foot aluminum extension ladder, but
I did all my early roofing, painting, general carpentry and
even tree work and pruning off this ladder. After awhile it
became painted on, dinged up, dogs bent and I just kept on
using it. Even after I bought two much longer aluminum
ladders for general work, I kept to this ugly one. After thirty
years, it's now a real ugly ladder. Co-workers would beg away
from it on the job with me; or else if they climbed on, insisting someone held the foot of the ladder at all times. It doesn't
reach high but much of your work will remain below twelve
feet, anyway. Finally, one day the ladder looked even perilous
for me to use, and I decided to break the extensions apart. I
would keep one as an all-purpose catchall work ladder—
something to use on the fly to reach a little higher. And the
other half, I painted the same color and locked on tight to
the steel roof we would install on our house in the summer

of 2003. The perfect roof ladder to reach the chimney for any emergencies and cleaning. Hooked from above over the ridge and then strapped at the base with two screws that hold it strong. Added to the ladder is a rope line that stretches across half of the roof and back to the second floor porch off our bedroom. The rope is tied onto the porch rail. If someone courageous needs to reach the ladder for any reason, the rope is there to guide. The steel roofing will be iffy to walk on, mostso in the middle of a winter night with a chimney fire added in. Hail to the roof ladder. Use it in the spring and fall, and keep that chimney clean.

CHIMNEY BRUSH

I bought mine after my first chimney fire a very long time
ago when an old timer told me, by-gosh, I could sweep my
chimney out with only a sack loaded with bulky straw. I tried
that. Still had a chimney fire (which will scare you). I went
out the next day and broke down and bought the real deal.
It was made for an eight-inch pipe, which was all I had for a
chimney at the time. The eight-inch pipe was actually situated
inside an outer ten-inch pipe that I had concocted as sort of
a self-made insulated-pipe. This was before the manufactured
insulation pipe that came on the market some years later. By
then we had moved out of the cabin and that dangerous
double pipe invention and into the red colonial farmhouse
nearby. You guessed it — my minister friend for whom I was
caretaker of his cabin and farmhouse, ended up selling us
both buildings and the property. Now, what I had worked on
for him, was ours. The eight-inch pipe brush was hung on
a hook and a chimney brush was bought to fit the farmhouse
one-flue clay-lined chimney. This we would sweep almost
religiously twice each year but not before getting hired out
to clean a clutch of other chimneys for other folks which
helped pay off the brush very quickly. It would eventually take
a faulty woodstove to scare us up our next chimney fire —
years after the first — and of course, a complete surprise. I had
started a morning fire before daylight and thought things

were going along nicely but *what in the world was that loud truck roaring by?* It was no truck. The chimney was on fire and roaring. It scared the death out of our seven-year-old son, while it was doing the same to us, but we were too busy scurrying onto the roof.

This was before the roof ladder I now recommend. With a layer of ice and light overnight snow on the shingles — but with a prayer and years of roofing experience — I somehow monkeyed up the roof and beside the fiery chimney. No doubt I was thinking of a house load of books and the people inside. I still can't remember if that was the fire I luckily doused with a neat spill of water aimed straight down the center of the chimney, or the time I cut a twenty foot sapling and climbed the roof with that pole to knock the fire out. Blame it all on a lousy Defiant woodstove with a cracked firewall and me thinking we could get by. We sold the Defiant to someone who said they would have the firewall repaired, and then we turned the earned money over for a Jotul woodstove for ourselves. Glass doors. Far less creosote headaches. With good habit, the chimney brush is still used twice each year.

HAMMER

I love my hammers. I own two 20-ounce Estwings that have been used on every house I have built, and mostly everything else. Only once in a great while do I become careless and use the claw of the hammer to start a hole in the dirt, and that's probably from my earth primitive stone builder ways. Otherwise, I own a bunch of other hammers—the hatchet shingle hammer, rubber and wood mallets, ballpeen, tack, stone and finish hammers. My first hammer for my first crew job, living away from home, was given to me by a friend who claimed she found it while walking in a field in New Jersey. Maybe so, and I kept it because she gave it to me. But I walked onto the job, kidded all day by my "toy" 16-ounce hammer that took much longer to pound in spikes. Out of pride I kept the hammer for that job but soon rose to the Estwings and stayed there. You quickly learn you can't help but have a pair of these. Plus, I have yet to use a nail gun, or even be close to one, but I see the shirtless roofers in the summer jabbing quickly across their job laying down plywood sheets with what may as well be a Tommy gun. *That ain't building, that's shooting and working the routine.* But then again, I'm only a one-man crew stuck away in the woods with plenty of work to do for one. And when my family is working alongside me, there's nothing better than sharing a hammer. It's tossable, and for some builders, it's still a rightful extension of their hand. My favorite story about a hammer begins when one of my Irish carpenter uncles on a roofing job took aim with his—being fed up by a nagging boss—and came within a few feet striking the man with the thrown hammer. This same uncle would live another fifty years working his various trades, and end up one day as a seventy-five-year-old Floridian, happy to lend his neighbor a hand with any repairs he might need on a roof. He climbed up on the roof of a much younger homeowner, and then that afternoon—while working on the patio around his swimming pool—was stabbed dead by a heart attack. Who would've thought? My uncle always talked of handing over his toolbox to me after he was gone. I knew his family never thought like he did, and I would never see his toolbox. So a long time ago when I built my toolbox, I built it like his.

BELLOWS

Bellows—a tool that is rarely used except around the kitchen wood cookstove, hangs up on one of our oak posts ready for any quick service. Bellows fits its name, and the look of it is archaic and absolutely practical. It blows air for you. In the sometime stubborn cookstove draft, it works wonders on balky days—a still air current, nothing much flowing—a few bursts from the bellows and the fire is moving. I could look up all sorts of historical background about the tool—where first invented and by whom—but I like sticking to knowing the tool as I found it, in this house when we moved in. One of the few possessions left behind by the former owners. Brass-tipped, wood paddles, and a flexible leather cushion. One can't imagine taking the bellows into a next life. If we ever move from this house, I'll promise to leave the bellows behind.

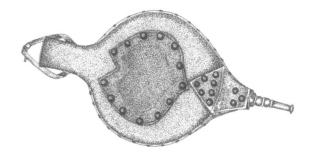

VISE

Do you you remember the vise and how it was used in the film *Casino*? It had to do with some surly guys and another guy's head. Well, I've never had to use a vise that way. I have no memory where my own vise came from—probably picked up at some barn sale, or given to me with a crate of other tools. I use it rarely, but have noticed whenever a plumber friend is around, we have copper pipe nine times out of ten rolled into the vise, cutting it to size. My vise is bolted down on the edge of my work bench which is nothing more than a few wide slab planks since covered with half-inch plywood. For the first twenty years the planks were smeared with paint and debris, and it was easier to just hide it over with a fresh cover and begin again.

Now that new surface is marked up with similar paint splatter and debris, and the vise works there. Re-bar gets cut in the vise. Molding coped. Metal sheets bent and formed. There's a small anvil style top to one edge of the vise where anything from screws to nails can be straightened, or something else stamped. I have brought back to almost normal chain saw bars whacked and warped from god knows what. Blade upright, I sharpen my axes in its hold.

I have seen large and very serious specimens called vises in machine shops, blacksmith galleys, vast mechanic garages. They look nothing much like the one I use but they all do the same thing—hold something tight—and crank the handle for tighter.

SUNSWUMTHRU A BUILDING

I really love my son but he isn't really convinced yet. And I can't say I blame him after living and working with me for eighteen years. It's been a tug of war much like my own relationship was with my father, except for a few differences. Carson is my only son. My father had four kids, and he did no physical work ever with me; we barely tossed a baseball back and forth. He was a lumberman and building contractor who put me into his business at age ten to learn the ropes around the real McCoys—builders, roofers, sheetrock stilt workers, plumbers, truck drivers, foremen, cynics, Vietnam vets, masons, farmers/sawmill men, salesmen, clerks, customers, complainers, railroad crews, goofballs, champs. It lasted from the ages of ten to nineteen, and I'm sure all of it was meant for me to learn the lumber business inside and out, and then head to a fine college, earn a degree and return home to the business. Forget about all this romantic whimsy of working outdoors with a crew of hardheads, tool aprons, maybe a radio on from one of the truck cabs, but working in a freshly cleared swath of forest with a dinky house going up in the clearing—who needed a radio? Woods were music. The business was a lumberyard staff selling products and going certainly batty amongst the camaraderie of other driven lunatics that just didn't look right, and it still doesn't to me. So I left home at nineteen feeling unloved and oh-woe-is-me from my family—the "kook" as they called me, and set up a life in the woods. I have written about this episode in another book but what saved me was the woods, a minister friend, and a woman I fell in love with, whom I am even more in love with thirty years later. That would be Susan, Carson's mother; and so when I feel he isn't feeling any love from me just yet, I don't worry with a mother like Susan. My co-worker, lover, eternal bride and, for Carson, the perfect eyes to behold after a tough day working with dad and you stomp back to the house and there she is. Solace. We would unwind the day, gradually, by sharing with Susan everything we had done together in the far corner of the backyard, on the woods edge, a glade we had opened a year earlier and heaped up giant brush piles from the trees cut. Firewood made. And inside that glade I found a brawny crop of ledge and began to work further until all trees, stumps, prickers and vines were cleared, and saw a building site revealed. Right there. Under our noses. A vista over the small farm pond, a brook trickling by, looking smack dab back at the house like it was always meant to be—for a cottage built upon it in the woods. When I excitedly mentioned this brainstorm to the little family of workers—Susan wiped her brow and smiled, nodding curiously. Carson turned his back, and I believe that was a moan I heard.

The idea of working together came from Carson at the age of fifteen when he decided he wanted to be home schooled. He just wasn't prepared for what that would entail. His first nine years of schooling had been in a small, community founded public school. It was a bus ride for him, and he went through all the hijinks of friendships, girlfriends, okay grades but mainly he was raised to love life to the fullest; so school became a place for a woodlander child to meet up with friends and spend the day. Schooling seemed, at best, an afterthought. He graduated with his buddies, and they all went off to the larger big-town high school where Carson watched his country school friendships break into little pieces of strict authority mixed with a wash of late 90s foul manners, brutal clichés and a miserable school environment. Top that off with Carson's ninth grade year landing in the era of The Columbine Massacre, so every week was, virtually, one more bomb scare. But the icing on the cake was when Carson came home one day after a year of this and admitted he had not only stopped reading books —amongst a tribe of nonreaders—but was indeed wasting his life away. He wanted help. He wanted to read again, hear real music again, feel his body again wake up and go to sleep with each day. That's when Susan and I decided to home school his remaining high school years; and at the same time I remembered the apron of ledge waiting up in the woods for that little cottage. We would divide schooling duties between the humanities and sciences, but for one year—from the summer of 2000-2001—we would celebrate the new century with building a cottage and attempt to put those good habits of book-learning and hand-learning together.

Let's just cut to the chase. Carson didn't like any of this

building idea, but he put up with it pretty well for a fifteen year old. I well remember my episodes of running off to hide in the lumberyard from my father's ideas of what he thought were best for me. The old bastards think they know just what is right for the youngsters, and so they will almost kill the relationship trying to teach them what they know best, and then throw in what they haven't any clue about knowing but hoping the kid won't catch on. Since we were working alongside one another—always doing what the other was doing—one was hoping a harmony would kick in, and it would for a few hours. Stamina is the first trying obstacle for any young worker. The other is to try to inspire and show the meaning and goodwill of what is being built—not only a building for all of us to use and share with others—but a communion between the workers as to what is built as a possible fraternity with one another and the tools; an actual two story building, with many windows, and it was made by us both. Carson would learn this the hard way, as I did with my father and would again with my son. It's all part of growing up—never stopping, no matter how old you may think you are. What I learned, is that no matter how much I may have thought my father was an asshole to me while growing up, I was now an asshole to Carson, and it took having a son of my own to see that father in my father could be me. I also spotted the other asshole—the one I was as a kid, working with the kid I was now working with. Was I that bad? A humbling revelation that day you are holding the long and heavy 4 x 4 joists for the second floor all by yourself on

a stepladder and your son is running off for his life, scream-
ing insults because of whatever insulting remarks you have
been barking at him to perform an impossible job between
two arguing nitwits who refuse to function. Then and there,
you suddenly see the young boy in you once upon a time
running for his life, and vowing never to become like the
father you once had. If there's any moment of eureka for a
father, this is it. And the hardest job in the world will be how
to grasp it with both hands, embrace it with all your might
and realize: what-is-his-is-yours-is-his. Take this moment, this
problem, and work it over and over until smooth. Like a stone
lifted out of a brook smooth. Allow your days working with
all these tools in all this building construction to be not only
working with one's body and mind, but working a respect
for one another—water smoothing—a respect for every tool,
pine plank, long spike, heavy load. That I have this boy in the
first place to be with me. Trying to work. Is there a greater
tool before me I have yet to learn?

So it was touch and go, like any love affair, but we got through
it. The building we had in mind would be two stories,
flashed with many windows, because I had a stash on hand
saved from other jobs, and because the building would have
no electricity except what we cobbled by extension cords; so
we would make lighting for inside the cottage by its correct
placement for natural light and how best the windows
would be set. There was a picture window pulled from our
house long ago during renovations, and I always thought I

would find a place for it, and sure enough it would be ideal overlooking the farm pond from the cottage. Otherwise it was double-hung windows all around the first floor, hand-made from sashes picked up at tag sales, and even a few from the side of the road tossed out as the trash by some home-owner. A wide Dutch door brought you inside — doubled-up pine planks swung by heavy black strap hinges. The floor was the same wide pine planks. Carson learned his nailing on the softwood, subfloor, varied width boards. I would snap a chalk line, and he'd go to work. While he was on that, I was laying up more dry stone under the pressure-treated sills. The whole kit 'n caboodle balancing atop that wider than the building crop of ledge. The heaviest corner stones we could find were placed strategically for the sills, and re-bar was drilled down through the sills and into the rock. On the day we started building, it would be one month's worth of mainly laying stonework up off the ledge and forming the sills into a building size square deck. I would wrench my back on the first day attempting to shift boulder size stones into locked positions. The injury only became worse because we were working that month off ledge, two sides level ground and two sides sheer cliff. A smarter man might have quit while he was ahead. But I was nuts for working alongside my son, despite the odds. When the month was over and we had the stone gathered, laid up, and a deck shown, we nodded to one another with a little knowing and earned smirk.

So Carson runs off during the most difficult moments of the

job. Nice guy, eh? I'm left hanging there trying to lift all the 4 x 4 joists into place. And then another time nailing down the hemlock purlins on the rafters for steel roofing. There were probably a few other examples, but time and the lovely cottage finished a few years now and sitting up there in the morning light, snow snug around it, has me forgetting the worst and only chuckling aloud as I write. No neighbors are in sight of where we live—woods between—but Susan would visit in the late afternoon and warn us how loud we sounded arguing; or were we laughing? Maybe singing? Was that shouting going on, she would wander from the house, coming out to take a peek. Sometimes—and sometimes madcap dizzy laughing chatter as my co-worker and I spoke favorite lines from films we loved and watched since he was a baby. You see, my co-worker had watched about a film a day with me since he was born, and each day we went to work with a combined solid duty discipline that could collapse into fractured flickers nonsense—provided, of course, all work was going smoothly. Susan timed her visits to the sound of laughter. And the roof went on.

Before the cottage construction was even begun, Carson learned the source of all our lumber. I had made friends with a local sawmill operator we hired to cut timber on our land. He arrived one day to scale the property with us on foot. Stumpage was sized up, a schedule for bringing in one of his choppers and what amount of pay we would receive for logs sold. When we were talking over at his mill, my eye began to look around. I saw pine planks, neat on stickers, piled nearly twenty-feet high, and 4 x 4 twelve-footers close by. There was enough there, easily, to stud our cottage post and beam style, plus all the flooring and roof dimension, with enough left over to build a door, trim the windows inside and out, and even make bookcases. Nodding at the lumber pile, I asked my new friend what it might cost to truck it all over. Because he wanted the logging job from us—and because I knew that—plus the lumber wasn't high quality but ideal enough for our purposes, we had a deal worked out with a nod, a wink and a handshake. Some hundreds of dollars. All rough wood but nicely milled so it felt furry rather than coarse. My friend had it delivered down to our yard by that late afternoon. Since he couldn't get smack up to the building site, we settled for 100 feet off (the pond was in the way). We would carry every stick of wood over to the site as we needed it, often lugging all the subfloor to the site after supper as a family event, and there it was ready for us in the early morning to begin work. Make as much work as you can as play and you'll enjoy yourself more.

In case you are keeping score, the subwalls I caved-in by using half-inch plywood; not being able to locate enough sawmill boards and wanting to save everything I had for the finish floor downstairs. The second floor would be adequate with just the subfloor wide plank pine, straight over the doubled up 4 x 4 joists, left exposed. A large, attractive carpet upstairs over the subfloor took care of any appearance. The

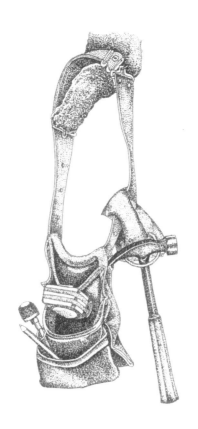

roof was a snow-shedding 12/12 but I lifted up knee walls on each side to fit in eyebrow windows running alongside for a view of the pond and house. The other side wall went to full bookcases since the cottage was also being built as a study in the woods and annex from overstock in our home bookshop. The gable ends spread to as much window glass as possible, to cut down on plywood application since both ends were at a killer height off a dangerous ledge footing.

When my lumberman savvy father came to pay his one and only visit to the cottage, he glanced around and asked, "Why all the glass?" He built his suburban homes wisely for uniformity and maintenance care. We built a cottage in the woods with no electricity, or plumbing, or really any semblance that man was welcome. But he is. After a walk through the woods—into a view of field stone and cedar shingle siding blending to a weathered familiarity—a roof top the color of leafed trees and the farm pond catching this building and the trees in its reflection, man will see he isn't really the all dominating force. You will come to the door and like to step inside.

When done with the job after a year, Carson knew the names of every tool we used. He also knew where and how to put them away. How to handle things. Right down to the distinguishing art when separating aside a 6-penny from an 8-penny nail. He had been on jobs where one was used properly, where the other one couldn't be. He knew how to work levels, how to plumb side walls, the importance of bracing. How to mix mortar, how to clean the mud tray and all masonry tools. How much a wheelbarrow could load and hold and come long distances across the backyard. How to toenail, how to use a handsaw, how to keep his index finger down along the saw handle for a straight bead. How to hold one end of a stretched out chalk line. How to almost wait. How to think of the other guy when he lifts, swings, throws. How to stop complaining and begin carrying heavy planks for hours at a time to the job site. To see how those boards will look that he carried as the floor he later walked on. To smell, how dear the busted open cedar shingle bundle is. To feel how unified the music he loves to listen to is now in a hard worked body—what a great song that is while nailing! To peek into the crawl space under the building—all that ledge hidden now—and once we were a month in there working upwards. To go to the building and know that a family built it, your own. To come out of the door one day and not be surprised a bird sings to you. Or the rain falls not quite far enough away from the steps—better luck next time. This building, this job, will be the one remembered into all the next.

After a year of building and the cottage was almost done (there is always interior painting to do), a carpenter paid us a surprise visit. He drove his good looking pickup truck into the yard, climbed out and left his wife in the cab. A friendly guy, about my size and about my age, with a beard. He was asking directions coming north a few hours from Connecticut and almost admitting he was lost. Then he started to look around. He saw the stone cottage I had built for Carson's birth and really wanted a look at that. "May I?" he asked. So we walked across the yard to the pond and the woods edge and came inside the hut. With its full, natural stone ledge back wall, laid stone floor, and cozy upper loft. The carpenter couldn't stop from exclaiming his pleasure. Carson heard it all. The carpenter had always wanted to try his hand at stone work and so took great delight at seeking out unusual stone buildings. Soon enough he admitted to us he wasn't really lost but wanted an excuse to get closer to see these buildings. From the stone hut doorway he looked over the pond and up to the new cottage and declared, "Now, that's cute as a button." That's all I needed to hear after a year of work, my son enjoying this visitor with me, and his declarations of approval—and what's more, our visitor sleuthing to be at the building site with us. A fellow worker. There's nothing like one.

WHEELBARROW

I started out over thirty years ago in my cabin years with one I found leaning up against the back of the building. We became partners for the next ten years. Already mottled with dry, caked mortar from a previous owner and probably left behind after a job as used-up. Not worth taking. Wood handles, metal tray and metal wheel. Old style. We started work together moving a line of road stone wall that I began rebuilding my first year at learning this trade. It was right outside my doorway asking to be rebuilt. Without a vehicle of any kind, the wheelbarrow is what I owned to transport stone, firewood, gravel, dirt, cut kindling from the woodlot. When I mixed mortar on jobs I used the wheelbarrow, and would wash it down afterwards forgetting what mortar I couldn't clean was the old mortar already there. It always frustrated me. When Susan moved in, she began to take the wheelbarrow up the power line that drove through the property, to scrub up for firewood, dead limbs and tops scattered either side of the right-of-way. I have a favorite photograph of her at work with a bow saw, blue dress and wheelbarrow. The wheelbarrow would move with us—probably with something in it—up the power line from the cabin to the farmhouse when we bought all the property from the minister. I can remember rebuilding all the stone walls up there the same way I did all the walls around the cabin. Same wheelbarrow; until some years later it broke down. Maybe it snapped off a handle, or the metal wheel just became a sore point. What with wide bouncing tires now on newer models, it was time to go with one of those. It was like graduating from a jeep to a limousine. I kept the old wheelbarrow until it literally fell to pieces and then hung it up on a low tree branch in the woods that I could see from the yard. The new wheelbarrow did everything the old one did, and better—but not quite with the same clunky, manual sound which is just the point of a wheelbarrow. I even picked up a second wheelbarrow, used, from a friend who gave it to me knowing my hand-hauling fetish. Now my son uses one while I use the other, often moving cords of firewood from one corner of the yard into the big woodshed. You want to race wheelbarrows sometimes when doing this. So we do.

SHOVEL

I first learned how to use a shovel amongst carpenters who called it an "idiot stick"—I guess to sum up who you were if you were forced to make a living with one. "We idiots." I was fifteen years old and laying in leech fields by hand under a grueling New England summer sun. My old-school father said the heat blisters on my lips from the work were good for me. He, who wasn't one of the idiots. But he would hire idiots to come and shovel snow from his neighborhood driveway, and later I took over from that bunched up crew of woolen figures. Long before regular snowplows. I headed to Vermont earning a living for over three decades using a shovel—digging waterlines by hand, septic pipe drainage ditches, turning old field sections into gardens, spreading crushed stone, digging foundation pier pits, making starter course ditches for stonework, and ho! shoveling snow, snow, snow. There is a village of homes less than two miles from our river valley home, and I easily shoveled every house driveway up there by hand at one time, or cleared their house roofs. Some barns. Old sheds. One vast, foolishly flat, two-car garage. There was one particular driveway where I shoveled snow, and a pathway that led to a suspension bridge, and then all of the bridge. I would sometimes take half a day just for that job, depending on the snow drifts and how much the town grader pushed back in when plowing the road. One year a friend operated that grader, and I saw how easy it was to actually turn the blade so very little snow mushed back into the driveway. That was a learning experience. Now I'm of an age when the back-saver shovel is used by all of us. We own three. Plus a rack of regular dirt shovels, all sizes. I like to collect most anything that acts as a shovel, and there always comes a need for the tool. I have kept one heavyset snow shovel for thirty years just for chopping ice crust, and in the off-season it works as a general dust pan for yard work. We now shovel—between all the family —approximately 300 feet of snow paths and a driveway, after every snowfall. We need a path wide enough to bring groceries in a wheelbarrow from the truck parked close to the road. The other paths go around the house to bird feeders, laundry line, porch, the studio, and over to the old tool shed. Only the faraway cottage and stone hut are without paths to their doors. That's the job of snowshoes.

SNOWSHOES

I would have no idea how to live without them. They mean as much to me as an old friend. My snowshoes are all ash wood made and gut-webbed design. Bearpaw, Alaskan and a few others I now forget what they're named, but I know each one hung out in the tool room on high hooks to keep the nibbling mice off, just so they aren't damaged. When younger, I went everywhere in this valley on a pair, including miles straight up or down the river ice. Strolled both mountain ridges either side of the river, tramping eastward deeply and west. And once, Susan and I left home with our dog Blackbird, a loyal Labrador pup, but after twelve miles of field and woods trouping, she became bewildered by it all. The first sign that we had gone too far was how our lunch sandwiches were frozen solid by the time we remembered to eat; and Blackbird whining all the way home, attempting to clean out her iced sore paws every few feet. Blame it on snowshoes, we were invincible in our 20s and 30s, with a pair. Worked on them when snow became too deep to hike into the woodlot to cut trees. Brushed a sealer onto each pair before every winter. Kept them out in the cold so not to warp the wood. We got so good we could race wearing snowshoes in a run. We liked best sitting on the Alaskan shoes and sledding down a steep hill when one came up in a hike. We've become confused by the new and expensive compact snowshoes dressed out in light webbing and aluminum tubing. There's a crampon underneath each shoe making for excellent grabbing. It's nearly effortless to move sideways and around on these. Compared to our snowshoes, the old ones now feel almost like wearing canoe paddles. However, the old shoes are made of wood, feeling natural beside the jiffy tube models. They look gorgeous when crossing an open field and mushing in long strides. Have that stoic prowess hung up on any wall— not yet meant to be termed antiques, since we're still using them. The idea of a tool should be efficiency, but also the dynamics of where applied. On a winter night without a sound around, nor a light, and the woods are snow filling, I still like strapping on my old Bearpaws and hiking off into these old woods.

SNOW-RAKE

In snow country—along with a pair of snowshoes, splitting maul and a few other tools—the snow-rake is a must. I'm not sure what we'd all do without one. Even amongst the steel roof buildings that usually take care of themselves, the rake still comes in handy. Before the aluminum snow-rake arrived on the market, I would make my own tool out of a 2 x 4 with a plank draw-blade screwed onto the butt end. It was heavy, but it worked okay. I have even used the snow-rake on flat roof jobs when my back was bad and the job just had to be done. I could pull the snow towards me with the rake and get the roof cleared. With a tube handle that comes with extensions that either snap into place or are worked with a wing-nut, the worker's reach can manipulate most roof jobs. Working the job up on a ladder, your reach is even greater. I now have three snow-rakes: first a bought one that I basically kicked to pieces over many long winter seasons, and naturally I repaired the blade with scrap metal and my pop-rivet gun. Then another showed up at some tag sale in the spring (buy in the spring and think only of next winter), and the third appeared when someone moved out of a nearby house with no desire of taking along any reminder of this snowy life. So I took it home. And you can bet, all three of us now use all three rakes.

JACKS

So my back is killing me for some time, and while it is being cared for by intermittent medical sessions, I decide to take on a job down the road from where we live. It's for a house I built twenty years ago. A good size, two-and-half story structure from back in that era when land could still be bought by a young couple, and a simple enough home built by any sort of builder hiding out in the woods. I was but one. Another carpenter friend and I hand dug fourteen foundation piers made of large chimney blocks filled solid with cement. No flimsy sonotubes for us. The house would rest on 8 x 8 hemlock sills soaked in green Cuprinol—the preservative of choice at the time—right on the cusp of when pressure-treated lumber would begin to storm the market. To add fun to the job, we cut in all the sills with handsaws and chisels, and of course it took forever. There was no electricity this far down the woods road yet, and it would take almost a year for any to appear. The landowners and builders were all working on a notion that nothing was impossible, so full steam ahead we blazed in a clearing I chopped out of mainly tall, weedy poplar trees. We even worked under the mystical notion that water for the house would-just-be-found. Luckily it was—first by a dowser that turned out to be a back hoe operator, who turned out to disappear after the job was done and who was nowhere to be found when the dug well went dry. The gods got back at him, some months later, when one of his dozer operators turned up as a favor for me and nearly spilled off the cliff edge where the house was situated. A lucky oak stump, from one of the trees I had dropped when clearing the house site, caught the bulldozer from tumbling over. Now years later, I hike up to the house and all these memories come rushing back. Because the dozer operator was shaken and just wanted the machine and himself out of there, and his dowser phantom boss didn't answer my calls, the landscaping work was never scalloped properly around the house. Ground water from the wooded hills spread under the building, along with rain spilling off from the long steel roof. My warnings to the owners went unheeded after the usual complications of their moving away and renting the house. Throw in a divorce and raising a family, and the place was left to take care of itself. It did pretty well, except for all this moisture beneath the house causing rot to occur from piled up sediment against the floor joists. I thought there was a mushy bounce to the floor when I was hired to renovate all the interior after some long-term tenants moved away. Susan, Carson and I repainted or stained every wall, trim, stairway, window and cabinet. And when we got down to doing over the floors, I felt trouble along the entire back side of the house, so I went to take a peek. The old 8 x 8 sills were solid all around, while the stout block piers looked like they had been poured a few months ago. But the 2 x 10 floor joists running the thirty-foot width of the house, twelve feet long, were shot. So shot, that when I shimmied my way in on my stomach for a look under the house, I could tear away handfuls of wood with any grab from a troubled joist. The moist sediment had done its terrible business, and not much was holding the floor above from collapsing down on me. Ever see a man move any faster out of a crawl space? Probably not. I telephoned my friend who owned the house and explained the trouble. She okayed any work repairs, and Carson and I started on it almost immediately. Building our cottage would now show itself for the good, the bad or the ugly as we went to work once again as a team. But with one added bonus—now we would be paid for our work.

Shovels, pry-bars, cat's paws, chisels, many varied hammers, levels, power-saw, handsaws and housejacks are what you bring to a job like this. Plus a truck load of handpicked pressure-treated 2 x 10s for new floor joists, and any extra to be used as bracing. You arrive on the job. Unwind extension cords for drop lights and tools and then stand there for a moment deciding how best to get under the house. Where we have to work—at the back end of the house—is choked with dirt. The front of the house is three feet above grade and easy to crawl under but a long way off from the troubled area, and many foundation piers are in the way. We decide to hand dig two entry ditches from opposite sides at the back of the house to at least open some light and ventilate the working area. When done with the job, we will install casement cellar windows with wells, in the aftermath of the ditch work. For now, we have to break in under the house with two deep ditches, because as we work in and under the house, all dirt and sediment has to be cleared away from under the floor joists and passed back into refilling part of each ditch. By the time we are done with this we have two mighty mounds of dirt, plus a well worn in work area on either end of the house to begin passing through new lumber to start building a renovated frame. The digging takes two or three days. Carson loves me.

The rest of the job is just common sense and getting very dirty. We have about a foot of space between the rotten joists and the ground to do our work. It sounds horrible until we decide to slide in sheets of poly to work on, and now everything is looking better. Not spacious, not easy, still dangerous, but a little cleaner. Tools can actually slide across the poly sheets. Housejacks can't—each one needs to be handed in, and I find out in time how my beloved screwjack is too tall in the cramped work space — so everything depends on my pair of shorter hydraulic jacks. Since I have done much of this work using only a flashlight to see, stringing in a cord for a drop light is like electricity has just been invented. Viola! We can see; the poly is under us, we may only be able to move on our stomachs or on our backs like eels, but with the warmth of the light and the clean plastic sheet underneath, it's almost feeling cozy under there. For one whole day I must not think about how tenderly rotten all the structure is above us—and I have my only son with me in this dangerous mess—while we fix in bracing with temporary jack-posts running down the first half dozen joists to replace. With each joist set two-foot on center we have about fifteen to tend to. We'll do it in sections. And at the same time, I decide to leave the rotten joists in place—with bracing under six or so—and with barely enough room imaginable, slip in new "sleeper" joists right beside the bad boys. This can be done—since the joists rest on top of the 8 x 8 sills—by passing the new joists over a crossbeam and into each bay. The joists will have to be angled in sideways, and with careful notching on either end, be lifted and tilted up into place. Any snugging up of the new joists can be done with shims placed under the notch work. It sounds easy enough, but it's hell. All work is on your back looking up one inch from the wood. The thought of the house collapsing onto you—what's worse, your son—runs giddy like minnows through your mind despite the fact you built the house, have now braced one section, and are still working in a coffin.

But it's the housejacks that pull you through. They always do. They are so determined and faithful if you keep them greased, like little work dogs in the dirt. And this is what we did for the next two weeks of slipping in new sleeper joists. Thankfully I had my young son running gopher errands in and out of the ditches for one tool or the other as I waited like a prone subterranean surgeon. Content that we had already worked on the cottage where Carson had the chance to learn about every tool, and how important it is to know which end of the board to send in and why. The dirt, from the ditch work

left over from under the house that had washed for years
down from the hill, we shoveled into our truck in four separate loads and brought it home for Susan's garden.

TYPEWRITERS

As I came upon a newly discovered typewriter at some yard sale or repair shop (the few left), it would spark some idea in me to write a new book. Once, at a popular flea market in southern Vermont, I bought a typewriter from the writer Alan Distler. I mention Alan because no one knows him much as a writer, but I came across one of his stories I liked in the *New American Review*, and then happened to be introduced to him by a mutual friend as two writers who should know one another. We smiled into each other's eyes with a nod. At that point Alan was earning a living as a school bus driver. One more survivor in these thar hills. At the flea market, as I carried away his typewriter for $15, Alan cried after me, "Write good work." Sound advice in three words, I'd say. I waved back to him. Olivetti, Remington, Smith-Corona and Olympia models are what I own, and the Olympia came to be my favorite—so I have two. Only the advent of the computer has cut a bit into my writing methods. I'm working on our living room iMac at the moment, wearing headphones, listening to music—which is an attempt to buffer the distractive surroundings. It's the warmest part of the house in the dead of winter; I can tend the woodstove, while editing as I go along with this musing on tools and work. Otherwise, I write poems by hand—especially the short ones, which, more often than not, are written in the head first on hikes in the woods.

Another book was written on Susan's Apple computer because I grew to like her upstairs corner nook after a long summer day building the cottage with Carson. I would come back to the house and have two, three, or four long poems spooling out from an all day reverie. The typewriter just hasn't that chatterbox ability, and these poems were meant to talk. The portable typewriters, built as long-term survivors despite the odds, are what I keep in my own study. Even typewriter ribbons have become like hen's teeth to find. The older I get, the look of the typewriter, and the fact of manual keys printing words that become lines on paper, reminds me of my stone wall builder self. And familiarity is important with any tool you wish to pick up and use.

TOOLBOX

Ten above zero early this morning, and thirty degrees warmer than yesterday morning, I walk out into the tool room to bring in my toolbox and be warm by the woodstove to describe for you what is in the box. No embellishments— just like I left it, and so find—slipped into one compartment two handsaws: 8-point crosscut and a smaller point finish saw, and always with me. Two Estwing framing hammers. One three-pound mallet. One tack hammer. What more do you need? One well worn cat's paw, pry-bar, and smaller pry-bar. A Swanson speed-square and larger rafter square. Three metal snips: left, right and straight cut. Vise-grips, various pliers, channel-locks and fencing pliers. Two keyhole saws, both with plaster dust on the blades. Two small German-made back saws which I seem to use constantly on quick cuts. A 100-foot measuring tape, a 25-foot Stanley tape, and Lufkin "red end" wood extension rule. When I started out, all carpenters used these with a sure wrist action. Approximately twenty screwdrivers of differing styles and dimensions (way too many). One hand-plane, one surform scraper, a block plane out of the toolbox on a shelf. One torpedo level; other longer levels are carried in my free hand when lugging the toolbox. Various electric wiring pliers—flat, long, bent & needle nose. Two awls. One compass. Two handy wrenches. A worn, scrub-by toothbrush. Four putty knives of different widths. A few cold chisels. Nail sets. Chalk line. Pencil & crayon stubs. Scissors. Some well beaten chisels (the better ones off in a toolbox all their own). A bevel. Various hex wrenches. Electric plug adapter. A half roll of black electrician's tape. Spare hacksaw blades. A few, used folded sheets of sandpaper. Many loose nails for just-in-case moments. And the toolbox built from one pine board with a strong closet dowel for its handle. Six compartments. About thirty years old. The general all-purpose toolbox we paw through all year long on jobs.

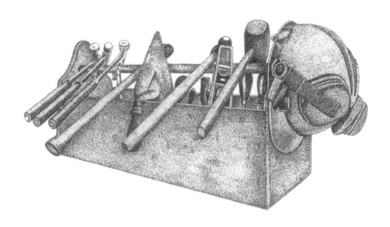

MORE SAWS

You're either a handsaw builder, or you're not. I've worked with carpenters who show up with a toolbox—in fact a whole truck—and no handsaw is in sight. Watching the handsaw disappear from hardware stores the last twenty years has been a sad phenomenon. Maybe two or three on display with Ace hardware emblems tick-tacked everywhere. Nothing like a whole rack of wonderful choice handsaws to behold. But then again, you are reading about a worker who has never used a chop-saw, or hardly been around one. It's the saw that is everywhere—even the gentle handyman on the weekend pulls out his chop-saw bench and goes to town. Since I prefer building with stone more than wood, I just watch the chop-saw take over and hang onto my handsaw ways ever more. I probably own sixteen handsaws—including a few cross, rip, back, coping, hack and even one Japanese tree saw for limbs and saplings. Another favorite of mine is the pole saw. Eight foot pole with a curved cutting blade and lopper scissors that work off a rope pull. The perfect companion for trimming fruit trees or most anything you can't easily reach. The builder's handsaw was a must when cutting spruce and hemlock 4 x 4 rafters and joists on both the stone hut and cottage jobs. My power saw could cut halfway through, and I didn't mind finishing the cut with my handsaw since I had built the stone hut without electricity and became acquainted with the quieter and rhythmic quality of the saw. You begin to miss it when it isn't any longer there. My Makita table saw is yet one more old partner. The safety guard has long since busted off, and perhaps like a fool I continue to work the saw with an open blade zinging. But no differently than the yard boss, Slim, running the shop table saw when I was a boy at my father's lumberyard, and we ripped out years of planks together on a Saturday morning. Learning to watch the blade. Handsaws all at once—building, tree, landscape—the trick is to make its movement your own movements. You might be surprised how you decrease your speed of life and begin to walk for pleasure again, talk and listen, write letters, read long forgotten great books, wait for the stars to appear. Imagine, waiting for the stars to appear. A handsaw might show you the way.

WHAT'S LEFT

What's left out in my tool room and sheds would be the
assortment of leaf rakes, steel rakes, crowbars, hoes, spades,
garden tools, iron bars, pickax, hatchets, hedge-shears, grass
clippers, brush loppers and even the gas powered Stihl weed-
whacker, and everyone of these tools gets a ride around the
yard in the wheelbarrow, or in the back of one of the trucks.
I can't live without any of them. I'm either doing stonework
with a few or getting hot and heavy with landscape work.
Don't overlook the importance of the weed-whacker at keeping a handsome stone wall clear of tall grass or brush. There
is nothing more disgraceful to a stone builder than to see his
work disappear behind lousy brush. I would work a hand
scythe, whip or sickle bar for years before the weed-whacker
came into play, but now I'm its key defender. It is noisy, gassy,
and this is talking only of the models that use plastic knives
or steel blades for cutting. In the right hands, you can watch
a whole field get cut over, an acre of alders brought down for
clearing, so many neat corners to the yard work. An hour per
week on our own yard and woods edge with the whacker and
I keep stonework, lawn and pathways in order. Between a pair
of scythes, three walk-behind brush hogs—one with sickle
bar and two rotary blade machines—plus a weed-whacker that
wouldn't die, I tended a gentleman's farm for twenty years
across town from where I live. I mowed his fields walking

behind those machines for hours each week. Luckily for him, he found a nut like me to do it for so long. But what better way to think, be outdoors (swallows diving for grasshoppers around me), and drive into the ground three brush-cutting machines. The scythe could last lifetimes but couldn't satisfy production wishes, so it stayed hung on a hook unless needed in a pinch. I made a living by using lawn mowers, too, but what's to remember after going through ten mowers over thirty years, except the one bought for $5 at a tag sale that worked the best and lasted the longest. And that weed-whacker from the farm job? It's twenty years old now and I'm still coaxing it along. Its way of being with me is a way for me still being with the couple that hired me all those years for their farm work; and this tool was bought—they thought—just for cutting.

LITTLE CHAIR

I have often wondered where we might find another one. It's child-size, and I can never seem to find another when looking, just in case we lose this one; nor have I any idea where we found this little chair in the first place. But it's a kitchen fixture. Sits there perfectly tucked beside an oak post and the wood burning cookstove. I've painted it already many coats of forest green, deep blue, turquoise and repaired any breaks to the short back spindles. Reglued the legs. Tightened braces with wood screws. We had the chair long before Carson was born, and afterwards it was his chair for years because he fit it just right. And we still used it, as always. For Susan, it's the handy chair to grab to reach a high cupboard. The chair to have when you're up first in the morning and rebuilding the wood fire, and this chair is where you pull up close to the stove to be warm. I can always see Susan sitting on it with her knitting needles.

Visitors come and all other furniture is filled up quickly…get the little chair. Painting ceilings, trim, molding and you just don't want to go for the stepladder and all that clunk…get the little chair. Sometimes our cat Woody will be perched up on it—sitting, waiting, thinking, doing only what a cat can get away with. When he jumps off, I lift a foot onto the little chair and tie my boots.

AROUND THE HOUSE

A neighbor just called wondering if I had my Shop-Vac handy so he could borrow it for cleanup work on a chimney that workers just tore down inside his house. Ironically, I built that chimney years ago and didn't own a Shop-Vac then. The last one I owned was thrown out some time ago; or actually the canister of the vacuum was kept as an ideal shop waste basket, and what we bought it for, was replaced with what it was supposed to replace—the good ol' broom and dust pan.

We have three or four brooms around the house for sweeping the plank floors, plus one always in the woodshed and another at the back door for a quick snow sweep of the stone steps, and another in the truck. Its smaller brother—the whisk broom—is also used and I can think of three at least between the house and the truck. When the broom bristle is worn down to nearly a nub, we like to use the brooms as hockey sticks out on the pond ice. When finished there, I cut the handle off and stick it in my dowel barrel of various round wood and moldings to be picked up for use on some carpentry job. The Shop-Vac is cumbersome compared to this unique tool, the broom. You always have to lug it in, always have to have an electric outlet handy, and it often becomes clogged up. Our regular vacuum cleaner for housework, we have learned to buy used models. It tends to a few rugs, and is essential when cleaning the finest debris the broom misses around the woodstoves.

Around the cookstove is another tool I like—the lid lifter—it's just like the handle wrench for the Jotul stove. We can't live without either one. There really is no replacement. With our Ashley stove, from the cabin years, we could lift its top loading door with most anything, including a boot toe, but I always fashioned a scrap piece of hardwood that would soon be molded smooth from our handling. I keep the one that was a favorite—darkened by the wood heat—on my desk. The various fire pokers, coal scrappers and shovels, stovepipe cleaners and asbestos work gloves, and even soapstone boot warmers that all hang around our woodstoves, are old friends by now. Used constantly. The boot warmers are heated on the woodstove and then brushed around inside a cold bed. My blacksmith friend, Scott Tindall, made sure our fire poker was a true friend when he made one for us with a brass face grin on the handle end.

ASH PAN

Our new indigo blue Jotul woodstove with glass doors cost quite a bit of money, but it was worth every penny. If you like your woodstoves—one look at this one—and you want this one. It was a hands-down favorite when searching to buy a new stove after limping through decades with stoves that were heavy iron, somewhat efficient but certainly not beauties like this Norwegian stove. We helped pay it off by selling a well-used Defiant woodstove with a doozy of a hole in its firewall. *I patched it and I patched it,* might go the song I would sing the last ten years of the stove's use. We had bought a replacement kit for the stove's interior liner but just never got around to it. Tearing the stove apart seemed what shouldn't have to happen to something weighing several hundred pounds. So we sold the kit and the stove to an ambitious wunderkind who was up to do the job. And then we sold a "Papa" Fisher stove—a few fire bricks were cracked, that's all—to another eager beaver. With that money earned, we had half the money for our Jotul. It was delivered to us, at a cost, by two guys with a clever mechanical handcart that worked like one part old handcart (another tool I like) and forklift. Come to a high door threshold with your load and with a press of a button, the load is lifted and ready to make its next move into the room. It wasn't quite as miraculous to see as two workers I once watched lift a very wide and heavy refrigerator into a house using only straps wrapped around their torsos. Don't ask me how, I was too busy smiling. Or the time our farm friend, Alden Bell, and I moved the cookstove from out of our cabin, onto his hay wagon and then to our house. I remember we cut round and straight saplings and set those under planks and rolled the stove aboard the planks across the room and on and later off the wagon. I have a story about how I moved a Home Comfort cookstove all by myself, with no tools used, into someone's house, but I'll save that heroic tale for the guy I did it for. The better story is how we discovered the Jotul only had one ash pan, as it built up a daily mouthful of hot coals, which required another pan to be swapped into its place. What to do? The stove company, of course, wanted an arm and a leg for an extra ash pan, so I took measurements and looked around. I had some sheets of metal left over from roof work and cut out two smooth panels. Then with the vise, rubber mallet, drill and pop-rivets, I bent and formed and screwed together a near facsimile. Naturally, it's uglier than the factory made, but it fits just the same.

WOODEN SPOON

Every country kitchen has one, not two, just this one real McCoy. The one you always use. The one you always go looking for—even with two or three other ones—and people are trying to help by handing you just any wooden spoon. But it isn't your wooden spoon. The job stops until you locate it. This isn't my tool. This is Susan's. She has had it as long as we have been married, so thirty years. No doubt it started off in our cabin years like many of our favorite tools coveted since then. I have watched her make cookies forever with this spoon, even after I bought a Kitchen Aid mixer for one of her Christmas gifts. I see her ladle spaghetti, clean out pots, the eternal slow stirrer of homemade, woodstove soups. The closest reminder to one of my tools, would be my framing hammer. One more tool just taken for granted by anyone else, but not by me. Of course it doesn't look like much of a spoon any longer—darkly seasoned and spiced and a smoothed-down-lip-of-a-thing. But it fits her hand.

FROM A TRICKLEDOWN TIME

There are two inspirational points for my building the studio, and neither have to do with Thoreau's cabin at Walden Pond. I built a somewhat model of that for myself at age fifteen in Cheshire, Massachusetts, beside a woods brook that ran through a gravel company, and it was all but three stone throws from my grandparents' home. A nearby gravel bank was where my younger brother ran his dirt-bike up and down in a gouged route of breakneck behavior, but at least someone from my family was visiting me down there *in the wilderness*.

The studio idea came from years of traveling coastal New England, particularly the outer edges of Maine, and all the little shacks, shanties, fishing huts that crop up—usually one room, often enough sided with wood shingles and a stovepipe poked out of a roof or side wall. Someone could be holed up in there quite comfortably. I thought after we built the cottage, I would build one of these for Susan. A place where she could have her weaving loom, skeins of wool, shelves of weaving and knitting books collected all these years. It would also be an ideal spot to store her telescope. On those best of starry nights she could easily pivot the magnified lenses right from the open doorway, facing southwest. It all sounded perfect for the summer months, but where we live has a winter-feeling half the year. We started to add up fuel logistics, a woodstove, running a cord from the house to the studio for electricity. Maybe the weaving studio in the house —small as it is—would be the better spot to stay put and pick up what warmth drifts up the stairs from the woodstoves. Not discouraged, I still went ahead with plans to build the studio for Susan and with Carson again as my working mate.

The second inspiration for the studio was one we had come upon on travels out west. Washington state, a ferry ride from a town port up a roaming narrow lake, gauged into the northern Cascades. The very same place Susan and I had once read about as youngsters in a *National Geographic*—this outpost from civilization—only reached by a ferry. From the photographs it looked as woolly and wild, and twenty-five years later we arrived, by happenstance, at this very spot, only to realize this was the place to take that ferry ride. We had landed here by accident—or in a homing pigeon sense— in our interest at driving further away from cities, towns, highways and, ending, what do you know, in our dream spot. Not much of a dream spot—yuppie gentrified by now—so we gazed up the long snakish lake as deeply into the mountainous Cascades that we could imagine and decided we would catch that ferry ride the next morning.

We stayed the night in a charming, Victorian bed & breakfast home that we had chanced on by an AAA guidebook. It was run by a very ditsy woman and her companion, who looked an awful lot like Alice B. Toklas and who prepared breakfast the next morning. We spent the night roaming a three story playpen of life-size doll mannequins in every room, plunked down on chairs, staring at us as we ascended any stairway. It all scared ten-year-old Carson half to death. We couldn't help but leap onto the ferry ride the next morning, where Carson was a card-shark, immensely enjoying himself playing hands with two blonde girls his age for most of the boat passage. There are many home schooled youngsters in this neck of the woods. On the other side of the voyage would be a small port with an ancient bus waiting for the few tourists, a general store and clientele of earnest newcomers, worn down locals and definite off-the-grid looking critters. It turned out these mysterious ones were moving about either on foot or in some rattletrap vehicle, but most seemed to just vanish from sight, as we would, too, on a trio of rented bicycles. This isn't Nantucket Island. The place is deep in high trees, a dabbed out clearing in the forest, a few roads spurring away from a settlement. We had overheard stories about leery Vietnam vets, hippies and homesteaders setup somewhere in hideouts and figured to go out thataway. And while bicycling, we came upon deserted vehicles pushed off to the side of the dirt road, pathways that opened momentarily only to be swallowed venus-flytrap-like by more jungle, no visible signs anywhere declaring "welcome." Our sort of place. So we kept up our bicycle tour until we lucked upon a unique hamlet of buildings—all huts and cabins and appearing deserted for the moment. Obviously, a special place by how well carved each building was, laid on stone, neat wood details around the windows, doors and roof line. Each built better than any bomb shelter; although, most definitely, the builder of these had this in mind. We snapped a few photographs.

Some years would go by, and I kept the photographs of the buildings as an idea. I actually made the cottage close to one, without even thinking about it, until looking again at the photographs a year after finishing construction. I didn't need the photographs—once seen out there in the tripwire forest, that cut of rough living in an age of computer vision—the magnificent homestead image was stamped in my mind. It would take a combination of a few things falling into place: Carson now skilled with some building habits, my year long struggle with a bad back melting off into a restored confidence to get back to work, plus friends were visiting from England and we needed to find a place for them to stay awhile. At first, we thought we could build the studio in time for their visit, and then the house job down the road—with the rotted floor joists—came up, and we did the repairs and also scored the house for our friends to stay in. We finished the house job a day or two before they arrived, and after a week of goofing off with them, we began the studio a day before they left. I remember the moment our friends drove up, saw the 12 X 12 size of the studio laid out with string, and the four corner post-holes hand dug. John Phillips, a fine poet from

Cornwall, his Slovene wife Jasna, and their three-year-old daughter Eva, would lend a hand lugging the 6 x 6 posts out of the truck over to the building site and onto saw horses. I wanted their family involved so we could think of them all helping us start the job off. The day they would leave and fly back home, Carson and I dug and set the four corner posts in. We measured off to square and plumbed the posts, back filled with crushed stone, and called it good on Susan's and my wedding anniversary…dusk falling around us…the end of August. If I recall correctly, Susan came out and took a snapshot of two very dirty workers.

That September weather had never been as beautiful. Maybe it was the work but Carson and I were bickering day after day, and we worked every day, but the days were glorious. Woods green blue skies all about us and we would start the morning off for five hours of work and then take a two-hour lunch break with Susan, music and books out on the lawn. You call this work?! Then we would go back to work until dusk, which I often did by myself at that point since father and son were bruised from nitpicking squabbles that I knew then were a nightmare but find hilarious to think of now. We would survive. Most of the time, I just wanted some time for myself laying up the stone that skirted the studio foundation—stonemasons are that way. Like the cottage, we had framed off the studio deck with pressure-treated sills and joists. The difference this time is that we would insulate the floor with one inch 4 x 8 insulation panels laid down right over the joists, forgo any subfloor, and set down wide pine planks for the finish floor then and there, cover the flooring with Typar building paper and go on with the job. The floor would now be down, sturdy for our business and protected until the roof was on. So during those late afternoons I would lay dry stone around as skirting for the studio, plus framing in a wide hatch-door to serve as a storage slot for plywood, boards and other building materials. I would rob stone from a stone wall I had built long ago that was right in the way of the studio. So no wall was lost. Where the studio would go, the stone would go right under it. Shimmed tight. The treated 6 x 6 exposed posts would be hidden behind old roof slate that I cut to size for each post and screwed into place. By the time the laid stone came around reaching toward a post, I just did my best at weaving the stonework together with the squared up slate. Matching colors is almost all of it. If it has nothing to do with structure or strength, fooling the eye is half of building right with stone.

With the deck ready for us and the stonework laid up tight, it looked like a pretty picture. From now on, I had all of the studio framed up exactly in my mind. One of our old doors from the house—with fifteen light glass—would be the entry door. Eight-over-twelve windows on the east and west walls, lovely for a cross draft breeze. Put one window on the east side that looks down toward the road and river, and a pair of windows on the yard and garden side. It will fill the studio with flowers. A large barn sash window saved from our cabin can be fixed on the north wall. With a new neighbor in our old cabin, it's best to set the window high on the wall and allow daylight, plus privacy. Tall and narrow barn sash windows will go either side of the glass door to add more natural light. We'll double up these sashes for the upstairs gable ends and allow the windows to open in. More of a cross breeze to fill the upper loft, reached by that apple picker's ladder I took away from the farm job. Well, I had to rebuild the wood rungs but the stringers were the same. Up there was a getaway spot, complete with a small bed and plenty of head room walking down the ridgepole. And this is where the late day sunshine spilled in through those gable windows and down onto both floors.

The studio would be easily half the size of the cottage. Built on flat ground. Fifty feet from the house, so almost an extension —but it was uncanny how visiting the studio on a beautiful Fall day was like being far away from home. Susan would come out and visit us, sitting on the stairway threshold. By those days we had all the first floor studded up with 2 x 6 hemlock, blocked for windows, plywood exterior walls on. Carson was now an old hand at nailing the plywood after I buttoned the corners on with him. He would be on that while I cut in my own window jambs and trim. Weeks went by and no sign of rain. One crystal day touching the next. We could hear the river as a constant companion. This working corner of the yard taken up with a lumber pile of dimension, pine boards, and 4 x 4 rafters being cut out for the roof. We were still working off the original delivery load of lumber brought two years ago for the cottage. By carefully mining our cache of lumber, we were able to use every last inch with only butt ends for waste—but not really waste—it was later dished into the kitchen cookstove kindling box. The rafters and floor joists would be the same rough pine as the cottage, and though I would rather have used stronger hemlock or spruce, the price was more than right, and there was a stockyard to choose from. We would double up the joists, left exposed, just like the cottage and build a short knee wall under the rafters, acting once again as structure long bookcases. With a steel roof down, and with even a steeper pitch than the cottage (live and learn), I wasn't too worried the softer pine couldn't carry the roof. Other carpenters might roll their eyes. Roll on, buddy.

It is a small and compact studio, but it would take some time for the three of us (Susan comes to the job for rafter help) to set the rafters in place. We worked off the second story— single layer pine planks—as our finish floor and perfect staging to raise up the rafters. Once the rafters are up on a building, it is a sight to behold. Let them have a day just to face the sunshine and under the stars. Don't rush to cover the roof if the weather is with you. Sleep up there on the loft looking past the rafters up into the night sky. Hear everything and nothing. I guarantee you will.

After the romance of the rafters has passed, we'll go cover

the roof with any pine boards left over from the flooring. We saved plenty that didn't make it for flooring, that are just right for roof purlins. Take a day to put those down, sizing up the gable overhangs to a foot long or better, and allow enough on the roof edge to shed the weather away from the building. Start at the bottom with the purlins and build a ladder-like system up the rafters letting the purlins be our staging. Even though it is a small roof, it will take one full day to get it all down right. Ten foot sheets, slippery handling ridge cap sections, and one roofer working with his son and wife who isn't at all happy about heights. But they both stick with me. The portable drill never had a bigger day.

We've now reached that spot where we are sitting up on the roof as father and son waiting to have one more steel sheet passed up by Susan. This is always the best part of any job. The roof height, overlooking the world, the brush of autumn foliage right before us on the hillside rising along the river. We perch up there and wonder why there were any problems on the job; or naively, even in the world. Sometimes all it takes is a hut somewhere in the world to be sitting on. Once, in those early weeks, while I was on my knees a few evenings laying stone, a worker for the rural utility company came driving up in his car to read our house electric meter. He parked in the drive and walked toward the house, ever wary for a startled dog, or even a person like myself popping a head up from behind his work and saying hello. That stopped him with a smile. He walked over—an older guy with the regular woods garb of flannel shirt and work boots. He had a million stories about his meter route of 2500 homes to tend and particular houses that had the meanest dogs. But he had a system down now. He carried meat bones for those snarling locations, along with a persuasive nature to train particular dogs to wait for him, on the day, tails wagging, for their treat. The dogs would hear him coming three houses away. A content grin to this fellow's face. He likes his stories. Likes the fact he took over the job from his ailing wife and her poor knees. She just couldn't do the walk-in on the rural cabins, meandering trails and deep snow. The opportunity for the job came up when he was laid off after many years working at a small cabinet factory. With the thought of wood, he rubs his hand along our new sills for the studio. His hand says he likes it. But it's the stone laid dry, fitted, large and small rock balanced and dynamic that always catches a country boy's eye. It brings out a smile that is saved for that special moment between two workers. We're in that secret musing of the mind where making something with something that costs nothing, but your hard labor, draws up a companionable sensation amongst strangers. Friends have been made forever in these conditions.

STENCIL BRUSHES

The studio was stoned up, framed, windowed, roofed and basically buttoned up through October. A two-month job. We even had the exterior painting of all the trim finished up for Halloween, brisk weather coming on. I worked days side-shingling the walls with cedar, hand cutting in small detail shingle patterns above the windows and along the midsection of the walls. The size of the building and shape only inspired these little touches. While I finished up the studio exterior work, Carson started moving firewood by small pickup truck —the dependable 1980 Volkswagen, diesel powered—out from the woods edge and into the big wood house. We like to stack firewood to the rafters. More times than not I climbed down off the ladder and walked over to lend a hand just for the change of handling split wood. By now, Susan had decided against moving her loom into the studio, and we thought it a better idea to turn the place into an annex from our book-shop; ideal for all the overflow of books. I built floor to ceiling bookcases on all walls and around all windows. The upper loft would be a book stash, as well as a nest for a nap. A place for a hearty guest to spend an overnight visit. We then buried an electric cord from my tool room so we could add a lamp or two for the studio, plus enjoy the portable record player out there. Summer meals would be carried from the house to the studio like a visit to Shangri-La. One bat found an upside-down roost on the north end, exposed ridgepole gable, and we called him a friend. Better than the red squirrel family that snuck behind a soffit on the cottage because we didn't close that off securely. The studio was buttoned up like a tuxedo. It sat through one long and deep snowed winter, and by the spring we cut off the building paper protecting the finish floor and looked down at our wide pine planks once more. Not much separation between the boards, but where there was, I cut to size long shim splices to lay into the gaps, then sanded all the floor. On other jobs I would often rub in a "puritan-pine" stain, though I liked this blond look to the wood, same as the cottage floor. With a smaller floor space it begged for an attractive scatter rug, but I thought of something else. Stencils. Over one spring day, the glass door wide open and on my knees, I stenciled a pattern of purple irises on the floor in a wide circular motif that mostly resembled a permanent rug. True to form, I got carried away with my stencils and brushes and added other designs to the wall woodwork and around the windows. It only adds movement

and thus space for the eye. Once upon a time, I stenciled every room in our house over many winter months with a radio on, listening to the Celtic games broadcasted by Johnny Most. Later, I was drawing over ceiling exposed floor joists, window trim, cabinets I built, whole rooms as wallpaper. In

Carson's childhood bedroom there are stenciled foxes running in one direction, tigers stalking the other way. Susan's in rhythm with the shuttle is still beating its own time in a small, snuggled room.

BREAD BOARD

From the best wood scraps of wide pine left over from the job, I made bread boards. One board for each of us to use. Simple to form into a shape—apple and stem design—with my jigsaw. A woodworker once visited and took a look at my cheap Craftsman jigsaw and announced that I should be working with a better tool. Probably so. But Susan bought this for me long ago when there was never any money, and I have become only accustomed to the tool. And maybe I like the fact it's an ugly duckling and still hangs in there with me. It made these bread boards without a complaint. We cut on them. Share them. Wash them off. And actually use them more as small serving trays. Made from scraps.

OTIK

I'll explain the title in a little while. Unless you're Czech, or brushed up on strange films from foreign lands, it might not mean anything to you anyway. It is the end of January 2004, a very cold month. A string of weeks where the night temperatures have been fifteen to twenty-five below zero and daytime hasn't crawled much higher than zero to ten above. It's now ten above and sunny where I have been working the last hour hauling in stove wood from an outer woodpile, four cord deep. The wood house is filled to the gills with seven cords of prized, dry hardwood, and we have another four cord of green wood seasoning for next winter over by the studio, where the sunlight falls the best. There is plenty of firewood. And a snowstorm is gearing up the east coast with one more beeline pointing to New England. At least it should warm up some for the snow to fall, but we're beginning to think it's just too cold for any snow to fall. Once this frigid weather begins to roll in and stay put and adds layers to itself night after night—those stars twinkling somehow —it is murder waiting for that depth of cold to flush out of a narrow, woods river valley. My long mustache just begins to melt as I come in from work, shedding only gloves and wool cap, so I can begin to type. This past month has also been an hour by hour vigil waiting for news from Kyoto, Japan, about our dear pal Cid Corman. Poet, translator, editor of *Origin*, who entered a hospital at the new year in his hometown with a heart attack, pneumonia and, finally, kidney failure. He's been hanging on in an ICU with his angel wife Shizumi at his side. A world community of poets stay in close touch by e-mail, raising money for Cid's medical costs, reading, writing and sharing poetry with one another. It's important to realize how poignant a poem is right now in this situation. That voice you need to have speaking to you. The finest poems have a companionable way, and Cid always knew this. The territory of silence in his poems is where he is, momentarily resting, as we all wait. I have roamed that territory the last three weeks. I'm all but convinced I am writing this book of tools, work and family, because Cid enjoyed my letters to him dealing with these themes. He always said it was a good thing to see a poet who made a living working with his hands—even better, with his family.

We visited with Cid, Shizumi and many poets and friends in October 2003 at a centenary celebration for the Wisconsin poet Lorine Niedecker. Cid is her literary executor, and he had generous contributions sent to him for a flight over from Japan to Milwaukee. Cid immediately shared part of this funding with us, so roundtrip train tickets could be reserved for our Vermont family. If Cid had his way, his family of poets from around the world would be with him for Lorine. Nobody said no. Cid's greatest wish was that all the poets would meet and become friends, and this seems to have happened. Carson was the youngest of the lot, learning to drink wine, mooching off a tribe of older pals eating Chinese or Thai, and running the lake blown streets of Milwaukee. It was a delight to see. In early May we had promised ourselves we would make this trip after we heard the good news from Cid. We had begun roof renovations on our house and would make the trip if the job got done—and come hell or high water this job would get done—for a newly built addition we would call Otik.

Cutting trees this winter southwest of the house shows a fine profile of the finished Otik. Red painted clapboards blending nicely with the rest of the house, and the tiny four-light eyebrow windows on the gable end and eight more windows strung across the front of the building. The same style windows that we framed on the second floor of the cottage. The same windows I cut into the house with only a drill and handsaws twenty-five years ago; setting back into place what was once yanked out. Battened old boards hiding the original window openings from inside. The windows always add that little touch of colonial New England. Looking over at Otik from the woodlot, cherry and maple logs in our arms lugged to a pile, one can see the hefty, visual return of our saltbox home. More of a girth now to the slope of the back roof. We moved in decades earlier to an austere and practical, deep-sloped back roof house. Maybe too austere and dark upstairs for a California girl like Susan. After a few years of living like our ancestors, I decided to knock out the roof in the hallway and build my first dormer. That was followed by another dormer in our bedroom, and finally one in Carson's bedroom. Three exact sized, hip-roofed dormers spread only wide enough between the three-foot-span of old chestnut roof beams. Someone—years before our arrival—wisely slipped beside each beam, new rough hemlock rafters, which modernized the place a wee bit. Its plank roof with asphalt shingles that I had once re-roofed on both sides of the house. Now was the time for shingle renewal, and I wasn't in the mood for tearing off two layers and nailing down new shingles again. The dormers had been our eyes to the backyard, small pond, stone hut, cottage and all the gardens. However, I had built a near flat roof addition off the original saltbox eaves in my late thirties, adding two extra rooms off from my study and the kitchen. Plus a bonus mud room. It was also many-windowed and galvanized a view of all the backyard and woods. But it was a miserable snow and ice catcher, and it leaked. Being on the north side of the house, the roof never saw the sun all winter. Ice jams happened like it was second nature, because it was. I would build this new addition, never thinking in my thirties what I would learn the hard way by the time I was in my forties—that you should build for your old age, especially if you love a house enough to want to stay in it most of your life. In my thirties, the thought of shoveling off a roof cake of snow, and smacking ice all day long, was an adventure. I did it for a living: what's one more roof? But this was an addition roof being spilled over by the large house roof, three dormers, and half the woodshed roof. Even Jack London would have begged for mercy! So by age fifty,

I had three troublemaker dormers staring at me, an old house roof, a woodshed steel roof which had been painted over with a sealer so it no longer leaked, but it also didn't slip snow off, and this ice-skating rink on the addition roof. It was time to make a move—thinking of myself at seventy years of age—and now with an eighteen-year-old son still at home willing to put in his fair share of community labor, but not believing his ears what was in the works.

It was simple. We would tear off all three dormers. Slip roofing paper temporarily over the dormer openings. And then begin to frame a whole new addition that would apron across the width of the house; starting the rafters a few feet above the dormer openings and running down eighteen feet to a three-foot high front wall where those string of eight eyebrow windows would go. If you can follow my drift—the eyebrow windows would be our new eyes to the backyard. The dormer openings would be framed up, in each room, with their old windows, now used as hatchway doors into the new space—Otik. Uninsulated. Unheated. Storage. A hideaway in the summer months, and hopefully an improvement over all the old roofs, ice headaches, and snow to shovel.

There would be less snow to shovel because we would build the roof of steel sheets, all one length, cut to order. We would also cover the upper portion of the old house roof with steel and have it all match. While we were at it, we bought more steel and renovated the big woodshed roof. It would be a month of tear-out and prep work on the new site. The sawzall would never be used as much again. Plus sledgehammers, crowbars, cat's paws, pry bars, handsaws, hammers. We could take out a dormer in a day—including moving it all down to the old barn foundation—to stack up what we couldn't salvage, for a bonfire over the winter. We saw we could save most of the dormer materials. The interior sheetrock was gone and so were the shingles. But the framing, planks, trim, windows, insulation batts and over half of the clapboards were all carefully pried off and saved. I came upon boards where a carpenter friend and I had once penciled onto the framing messages for the next carpenter to find— not realizing I would be the next carpenter —with my son as sidekick. I showed Carson the messages from twenty years earlier, feeling all at once both nostalgic, and fatherly humbled.

The roof is a 4/12 pitch, which isn't much, but certainly better than what we had. Rain washes off without a thought and maybe snow sticks awhile, but eventually it loosens and slides. The steel roof has its own powers. Screwed onto 2 x 4 spruce purlins over 2 x 10 rafters. We framed in a full partition wall underneath, halfway up the length of rafters to strengthen the roof. The only oddball plan was spacing the rafters to allow clearance for the use of the interior old dormer windows —now used as small glass doorways. I didn't want to inhibit our view out from the bedrooms and hallway, nor make less headroom when we ducked into Otik. The roof was already sloped down low enough. The old addition roof was now the Otik floor, and rugs were spread over its pitted, double coverage surface. Someday, I may lay down pine board flooring or do what we did on the studio loft—place fir luan sheets over the rough surface, then polyurethane it finished. For now we have a watch on how the interior of the steel roof will cooperate. I have always laid my steel roofs on purlins but it has mainly been over old barns, sheds, or unheated buildings. I have even strapped over old shingled roofs with no problem when screwing metal roofing down. But there can be moisture trouble with exposed steel roofing on the interior side, even in the unheated Otik. So late in the game, I was cutting in wall vents to beat the band to draw the best ventilation for condensation woes. I ended up cutting a wide vent opening in the old buried woodshed roof so we could, at least, draw some breeze from across the Otik's one gable end. This minor nightmare—on top of doing all the roofing with ten, twelve and eighteen foot long steel sheets, a mile of accessories and varied length screws (remember, three roofs were being done at once)—only added to the building being called Otik by Susan. The clincher was when I was down under the roof, shoved up into some corner, with my two lovely, misfit co-workers right above me sitting and waiting on the roof. We all could hear each other's every word and sniffle. I was in a pinch, once again, with not quite the right tool and banging at a nail or screw with whatever was handy and generally making it all sound like a royal conniption fit. Every worker knows some jobs just boil down to that moment.

It's going to rain any minute now, or else the hot sun is baking my ass under the steel. Plus I can't see what I'm doing. My two co-workers above me are, naturally, laughing at it all.

One wouldn't have expected Susan to take to Jan Svankmajer's film Little Otik. But then again it is about a woman and her newborn child who is somehow conceived from an old tree root and grows into this immense flesh eating monstrosity that causes all sorts of blood curdling racket, while retaining a domestic harmony and sweetness amongst the family it does love. What's not to love? We built Otik with our own hands, and have certainly earned the privilege to call it what we wish.

FORGOTTEN

How about the tools I'm going to forget? It's bound to happen. I look around the tool shed, big woodshed, dark corners of the outer work huts and seem to have most everything covered. Then Carson asked about the tar-mop. Oh yes, the tool we used every summer, on the hottest possible day, to spread liquid tar coating over the double coverage roof of the old addition. We don't have to worry about that job any longer—the roof is now the floor inside Otik. At the end of the sticky, miserable job, I would saw off the handle from the gunked mop and save that, throwing the rest away. It took kerosene rags to clean the ladder rungs, old sneakers, sawed off handle, our hands. Then there's the pocket knives, utility knives, garden tools like hoes, spades, tiny rakes...so I mention them now. Susan has a favorite spade I gave to her thirty years ago that an elder gardener gave to me when he thought his garden days were over. And the water hoses that we like having and certainly use over the summer; but we still keep handy our old habits of drawing water with a bucket from the river, from the pond, letting rainwater get caught in any bucket on its own. Just walking out now to make sure the woodshed door was closed—snow blowing in with a storm —I see I have forgotten to make note to my other roofing tools: metal and wood roof-staging-brackets, a roofing shovel that slides under and pulls up shingles, my slate roof nail-puller

—blade-like and welded extra long by a friend once upon a time. How about my sanders, chain-cutters, socket sets, China bristle paintbrushes that I would save house job after house job? Hard to throw those away. Don't forget the long and short wood and pipe clamps. I would be lost without them when putting down these wide plank, pine floors. Although, I'm certain to forget many other tools, maybe that's just the way. The reader is now here with me. May you fill in the gaps.

BOOK

I wrote this book for my son Carson, who has no idea, yet, how much he meant to me as a working companion. He's a musician and writer, a dreamer in that world, already successful at age eighteen; why does he need to be bothered by a father who loves to work with his hands, and to be a good sport about being part of all these building jobs? But he had no choice. While it was often a struggle, Carson also wished for home schooling, and this manual work schedule was often part of it. Along with his own secret ambition—sometimes whispered into my ear by his mother—that he was attracted to his dad and this working life. I know it has made him a finer writer, a more rhythmical body composer, a young man alert within more than one world. The next steps will be all his own. And however this world of personal work tools is remembered, I know I couldn't have built any cottage, studio, or Otik without him. By age fifty a carpenter needs a helper, needs a companion, needs someone he thinks he can teach something to. The wonder will be, that he will be taught in return. The best books are endless—a feeling that there are no real answers, no real solutions—that we are ever evolving but sticking to a course. Pages to be filled in later. A book as a tool, to be used from my life, to be given to another.

ABOUT THE AUTHOR

Bob Arnold lives in the Green Mountains of Vermont where he has long made his living as a builder, stonemason, poet, and bookseller. His many books of poetry and prose include *Where Rivers Meet, Once In Vermont, On Stone, American Train Letters, Invent A World,* and *Hiking Down From A Hillside Sky.* Since 1971, with Susan Arnold, he has edited books, anthologies, and journals from Longhouse. His ongoing *Woodburners* series is available online at: http://www.longhousepoetry.com/woodburnersnow.html

ABOUT THE ILLUSTRATOR

Laurie Clark, who was born in New York in 1949, now lives in a small fishing village on the east coast of Scotland. Her recent drawings are concerned with the infinite differences and similarities of plant forms. With the poet Thomas A. Clark she runs Cairn, an occasional space for contemporary art and ideas. Since 1973 their work has appeared together in numerous publications from their own Moschatel Press. Her illustrations have also been published by Wild Hawthorn Press, Coracle, and October Foundation.

This book has been designed by two-hands
in collaboration with Jonathan Greene. The typeface used
for the text is Joanna, designed by Eric Gill in 1930
initially for his own use. In 1937 The Monotype
Corporation made a version for machine
composition.